Dec. 2001

Ken —

Thank you —

R. L. Gregg

GRIGGS ANTHOLOGY
Joe Bellino's Thighs
2001

TANTALUS BOOKS

San Ramon, CA – Fort Collins, CO

JOE BELLINO'S THIGHS

Library of Congress Cataloging-in-Publication Data

Joe Bellino's Thighs.
    p.cm.—(Griggs Anthology)
Short stories, poems, and essays originally presented at the annual writing contest of the "Across the River" Writers' Roundtable
ISBN 0-922530-09-2
American literature – California – San Francisco Bay Area. 2. San Francisco Bay Area (Calif.) – Literary collections. 3. American literature – 20th century. I. "Across the River" Writers' Roundtable. II. Series.

PS572.S33 J64 1999
810.8'097946'09049—dc21   99-047795

Publisher: Rick Griggs, Tantalus Books
Editor: Fred Norman
Printed in the United States of America

10 9 8 7 6 5 4 3 2 1

You may order this book from your bookstore. This title may also be purchased from the publisher in quantity discounts.

For more information on the Across The River Writers Roundtable or Tantalus Books titles write or call:

Tantalus Books
San Ramon, CA
Fort Collins, CO
888-647-4447

Cover design by Lila Mingione

Joe Bellino's Thighs Sponsors

Book Design:
Lila Mingione
California Design Group
San Jose, California

Cover, Endsheets, Board Materials:
Mary Lou Slater
Ecological Fibers, Inc.
Lunenburg, Massachusetts

Book Printing & Book Binding
Publishers Press
Mountain States Bindery
Salt Lake City, Utah

From The Publisher

To the anonymous and hopeful writer huddled quietly, revising, in a small apartment or on a park bench—you are this year's "honored guest." It is our personal, past memory of you that keeps us humble today. It is our current contact with you that keeps us compassionate to pain and discouragement. Finally, it is a future glimpse of you, in the glorious, published spotlight, that keeps many of us doggedly scribbling so that we, like you, may be worthy.

Joe Bellino's Thighs? Several eyebrows shot up, cheeks twitched, but the work to prepare this feast continued. Blanche Abrams nourished the team with the food groups; Cynthia Bryant spoon-fed open mike night; Jerry Gervase provided "chicken soup for contest judges;" and Fred Norman arranged the ingredients for performing "culinary" editing miracles. The literary banquet was prepared as I nibbled and munched on ideas with our bookkeepers and accountants, designers and distributors, school administrators and English teachers. I've been blessed to have great cooks do the hard stuff so I could keep building the foundation.

Rick Griggs
San Ramon, California

From The Editor

I remember Joe Bellino. Navy. Late 1950's. Heisman Trophy Winner. I remember him running and running and running. At times, nobody could stop him. Army certainly couldn't stop him, and for a Marine, which I was then, that was as good as it got. But I don't remember his thighs, just his moves and the pleasure I felt watching perfection. He must have had thighs, though—man, he must have had thighs. And of course he did, for I trust a poet's recollections.

What a great title! A man's name lives on because of Robert McNally's wonderful poem and because of this anthology. However, I am saddened to have to say that this is the last Griggs Anthology that I will edit. I hope someone in the future will remember my efforts as I remember Joe Bellino's. He was a success, he played on a team, and if my anthology work was a success, it was because of our team: I want to thank Blanche Abrams for her ideas; Jeremiah Bryant, Bob Eastwood, Cathe Norman, and Camille Thompson for their typing and proofreading; Anastasia Syzrantseva and Sara Bernard for their office help and creativity; and all of the members of our writing group who made the writing contest possible and helped with this anthology in ways too numerous to list. But most of all, I want to thank Rick Griggs, our publisher and writing group founder. He gave writers an opportunity to publish and readers an opportunity to know a Joe Bellino and all of us an opportunity to better ourselves by bringing us into closer contact with the written word.

Fred Norman
San Ramon, California

Joe Bellino's Thighs
Contents

More Winners

. . . *And More Winners*

Joe Bellino's Thighs
Robert McNally

My mother fell in love with them: thewy, thick,
bulging beyond standard football pants.
A Naval Academy equipment manager split seams
from knee to crotch, stitched canvas into the breach
to make room. Sutured fabric straining against
    quadriceps
in *Life* magazine's precise black & white gave Mom's
    breath
pause. She looked long, then slid the issue
beneath the endtable stack, where my father,
who read rarely and only from the top, was sure
to miss it. He was still at work on Army-Navy game day
when she staked out a place in front of the TV,
watched the screen like a jenny in harness fixing
on plump cabbages beyond her reach,
while Bellino juked, jammed, and juiced downfield.
In the fourth quarter my father filled the doorway,
an Army veteran asking, "How are my guys doing?"
Mom eyed his legs; slacks bagged round them,
caught more air than flesh. "Navy's winning," she said,
lifting her gaze past him. "Wouldn't you know it,"
he announced, turning toward the kitchen
to pour whisky.

Lunch with a Marchesa
Jean Ohman

On the day of my lunch with the marchesa, Chris, the butler and house-boy, waited for me near the iron gate leading into a courtyard. Marchesa Fiamma had phoned me the previous day and I was just a little nervous. She is, after all, the daughter of Salvatore Ferragamo, the famous designer of shoes. Two months ago, after a long and intense interview, she agreed to let me rent an apartment in one wing of her stone *palazzo* in the center of Florence, Italy. Although I had talked with her a few times since moving in, I hadn't been in the main part of her house and had not expected to be fortunate enough to share her dining table.

Chris had often been in and out of my apartment, showing me how to use the stove, fixing a fuse and doing a variety of odd jobs to make my stay more comfortable. That day, he greeted me with his youthful smile, calming my slight apprehension. I followed him across the stone courtyard and waited while he opened the wooden door to the house. Leading me inside, he asked in Italian if I would like a glass of wine. I hesitated a moment, not knowing what was proper, but decided I was expected to have a glass before lunch. I brilliantly replied, "si grazie," assuming I understood him correctly and he wasn't saying something I shouldn't answer, "si," to. My Italian is quite limited.

As we entered a wood-paneled library, a man of about fifty rose from his brown, comfortably worn, leather chair. With an easy smile, he said, "Jean Ohman, I presume."

He's gorgeous, I thought, trying not to stare at this tall noble-looking man. His hair was dark, not as black as the marchesa's, but like his wife, his smile was warm and sincere. "I'm Giuseppe San Giuliano," he said, introducing himself. He's even more charming and attractive than I had imagined, I realized, as he immediately made me feel at ease.

Chris gave me a discreet smile when he returned to the room carrying my wine on a round silver tray. Soon after, Marchesa Fiamma joined us, thankfully also holding a glass of wine. She filled the room with an elegance that matched our surroundings. Looking cool and sophisticated in her salmon-colored silk blouse, she appeared more youthful than her age, which I guessed to be mid-forties. Long black hair brushed against her olive skin and fell across her shoulders. On her feet were exquisitely designed shoes. I looked down at my own and tried to make them inconspicuous.

We sipped Chardonnay in a room filled with books shelved in a choir stall, once found in a convent, that circled half the room. Photographs and portraits of the marchesa with her husband and children told the history of their family. Marble topped tables rested on a multi-colored Persian rug. Looking up, I smiled at playful cherubs peering down from a high-arched seventeenth century frescoed ceiling. I felt the smooth texture of worn leather as I relaxed in one of two brown chairs that had obviously been much used and greatly enjoyed by family and friends. The marchesa sat across the room in a more formal chair of ivory and red silk.

What does one say to a marchesa, I thought, wondering what our conversation would include. She knew we shared an interest in opera, classical music and art, and I was relieved to find them a major topic of discussion. During the past weeks, the marchesa had given me tickets to Handel's Messiah, and Moussorgsky's opera, Boris Godunov, when she and her husband were unable to attend. I described how although the opera lasted four hours, I was mesmerized by the powerful music, costumes, and masterful staging.

"I have a deep love of opera, but I especially enjoy Italian composers like Verdi and Puccini," the marchesa confessed. "I often listen to their recordings," she continued. We laughed when I mentioned how I delighted in hearing music drift through my window when she occasionally broke her busy schedule to come home for lunch. "No," I protested when she said, "I'll try to keep the volume down." I found myself hoping she would put on a recording while we sat there, but she didn't.

Lingering in that room decorated with art and antiques, silver vases and silk covered furniture, I thought about how easily I could slip into an aristocratic life. It was like being inside an opera set— I could hear the music inside my head. I felt totally comfortable. My nervousness disappeared and I felt at ease with my surroundings.

We left the library, moving through the living room into the dining room. Large windows, spanning the three rooms, opened onto a spacious garden, bringing the outside in and extending the already immense space. The garden was filled with broad leaf poplar trees, cypress, shrubs and ferns. I imagined summer nights there with wine, music, and a gentle breeze.

A long table, positioned between the windows and a marble fireplace, dominated the dining room. Centered on a white tablecloth were two silver candle holders, each about two feet high. The soft glow of candles and diffused light from an eighteenth century crystal chandelier illuminated the room.

Finding our places at the table, the room soon filled with energetic discussion. "Every time we looked closely at the walls or ceiling, fragments of another fresco appeared," the marchesa explained, as she described their renovation of the spacious rooms. "We think the *palazzo* dates back to the fifteenth century. It had extensive damage due to the ravages of floods and wear when we discovered it about twenty-four years ago," Marchese Giuseppe interjected.

Chris served lunch as our conversation continued. He had shed his house-boy jacket and was now dressed in a butler's uniform, complete with white gloves. Some of my nervousness returned when I realized he was standing at my side with an oval platter of penne pasta, expecting me to do something. I used the two silver serving utensils, trying to act as if I had been doing it all my life. Thankfully, I didn't spill. Silverware—lots of silverware—surrounded my plate. I fumbled, attempting to follow the marchesa's lead, but always served first, I could only hope I did the right thing. A crystal decanter of red wine stood beside each of our plates and Chris refilled our glasses throughout the meal. I felt rich and pampered and I loved every minute.

Conversation continued over our second course, which included meatballs, mashed potatoes and gravy. It didn't seem very Italian and I was curious about the menu. Could it be because of my Swedish/American heritage, I thought with amusement? We talked of my dog, Monty, an eleven-year-old Sheltie whom the marchesa almost refused when she interviewed me before agreeing to rent her apartment. Monty became known as "Piccolo Lassie" to our friends and the shopkeepers in the neighborhood. The marchesa explained that they had twenty-two dogs at their home in Sicily where her husband was born. "See, I told you I like dogs," she added.

We ended our meal with fresh slices of kiwi, then moved to the living room where Marchesa Fiamma served coffee. Pillows of gold and green silk fabric decorated the lemon-colored couches and chairs where we sat. On the wall, *trompe-l'oeil* frescoes created the illusion of walking through columns and temples of ancient Rome. I tried to keep from straining my neck as I looked up at angels floating in clouds on the

Renaissance paintings that filled the high-arched ceiling. It was like an opening into heaven.

Drinking rich black coffee, I expressed my gratitude for their invitation. I wanted to stay forever but knew the time for my departure had arrived. They walked me to the door and as we stood in the courtyard saying goodbye, Marchesa Fiamma looked toward the windows of my apartment in the second floor wing. Reflecting on our earlier conversation, she asked me, "Which operas are your favorites? When I turn the volume too loud, at least you should hear music you enjoy."

"All of them," I said, turning to leave. "All of them—as long as they are Italian."

The Melody of My Soul
Simmi Mehta

Yellows to oranges,
Reds become purples,
Colors envelop my eyes
Ablaze by the flame before me

My shadow awaits to the rear,
Dancing to the beat of the breeze
The fire within me suppressed
As I watch the one in front.
It consumes me-

I long to dance to the music of the wind,
To be me
But I am mesmerized by the colors in front

The wax melts-
The wick blackens-
The flame dies-
And I shall never be me,
Never dance to the melody of my soul

To My Sister
Sara Bernard

For hot chocolate
and days of molasses snow
those pale puke purple suits
encrusted with the melted stars...
For legos
the clink of Chinese checkers
and days of shaking Parcheesi dice
as the rain torrents fall outside...
For trees
and sour apples and chalky stones
slick stripes of reddish mud
days of you, and you and I...
For the bulgy stockings, it's barely dawn
For leaving the tiny night-light on
For cookie dough and a violin's screech
For holding your knowledge beyond my reach
For manipulating me, the nine-year-old slave
For snapping and screaming though my path you pave
For my car, my life, my me, my gain
For my tear-streaked nose pressed against the pane
    of the door you exit through

Forget I always loved but
thought I hated you...
diaries stabbed with frustrated phrases,
I'd eat my words a thousand times, but
your mind's flowing, twisting mazes
soft as sugar, sharp as limes
so hard to bear
so hard to be
accepted by your scornful glare
...now waiting for the ice to thaw
my pencil beauty shadows draw
joy pain fire pretty passion peace
your sweet smile's laughter crease
and the freckle on your lip.

Apple Pie
Laura Fischer

The whole family rode out to the country to get apples for pie. The San Joaquin sun crawled into the back seat and made us sweat. Pie wasn't on my diet, but if I had nothing else for dinner, I could count it as a fruit serving. At the fruit stand the Granny Smiths were small and green, piled in tattered wooden baskets tipped to show off the fruit.

"You girls pick out a sack," said Dad, and strode off down the road like the wagon master on the Wagon Train reruns. Our mother, Joanne, stayed in the car, legs flung out the open passenger door, fanning herself with one of my older sister Angie's hairstyling magazines.

"It's cooler out here, Joanne." I wanted to kick her for always hanging back, as if we weren't good enough. She waved the magazine and said nothing.

"C'mon." Angie tugged on my shirttail. "Just ignore her."

"She just sits there. She always just sits. It's *weird*. And Dad—where the hell does he go when he walks away?"

"Geez, Susan, don't let them hear you cuss." She sashayed toward the fruit stand. The boy minding the fruit stand had flaring red pimples, a sunburned crew cut, and a small silver hoop in his right ear. Angie flipped her hair and he stood up so fast that he sent a basket of apples rolling like baseballs over the wooden floor of the shack. We have the same blonde hair, but Angie's makes boys turn red in the face. Mine just hangs there.

I decided to scout the other end of the road, until the fruit stand and our dusty blue Escort were hidden around a bend in the road. No cars passed. Everyone had dropped off the earth but me. I flung my head back to kiss the July sun, just the two of us alone on the empty planet. After awhile I started back to the car, a dog at the end of its chain. When I reached the car, Dad and Angie were arguing over a black and white kitten that she held clutched next to her blue halter top.

"No cats."

"Her name's Panda." Angie ignored him.

"No cats."

Joanne spoke up. "Let her keep it."

Dad always crumbled when Joanne asked for something, as if his insides gave way when he heard her voice. On the way home, Angie and I sat with the kitten between us under an overturned apple basket. Panda's pink nose appeared between the loose slats of the basket and I offered my finger. She sniffed politely, as if considering her options. I rubbed her nose and her tiny motor kicked in. I looked up at Angie, who met my eyes and then turned to stare out the window.

As soon as we got home, Joanne headed for the stairs. "Just a little nap," she said.

"You said you'd make pie." I didn't even try not to sound whiny. She'd slept all the way home in the car.

"Later." Joanne slid her hand along the banister as she mounted the stairs. It looked blue and bony, as if she'd put on someone else's hands that morning.

"Why don't you make your own pie if you're so hungry," said Angie. She dangled her yellow hair ribbon in front of the tiny kitten, who swiped at it and rolled on its back.

"Maybe I will."

I went to the kitchen and rummaged through the cookbooks that stood in a neat row on the kitchen cabinet. I found an apple pie recipe on a sticky page in a yellowed cookbook. I found a cube of butter in the refrigerator, a chipped blue bowl in the bottom cabinet under the oven, and flour in the canister by the cookbooks.

"Careful," said Dad, taking a beer out of the refrigerator. "Don't let your mother catch you."

Joanne never let us in the kitchen. All our friends envied Angie and me because we never had to help with dinner or do the dishes. Joanne said we'd just mess things up. I watched cooking shows on TV instead, eager to learn the magic of individual ingredients that turned into stews and casseroles and pies.

I dumped flour and a stick of butter into the bowl. The flour flew into my eyes and hair. The butter lay in a clump in the middle of the bowl of flour and refused to mix. I found a spoon and squashed the butter, then stirred furiously. I added water, a little at a time, like the cookbook said, but I couldn't see the point and splashed the whole thing in at once. Finally, I squeezed the whole mess together with my hands.

I ended up with a lump in the bowl. "Close enough," I thought. I opened every cabinet in the kitchen, leaving sticky clumps of dough on the doors, until I located the rolling pin in a dark corner. I slapped the dough on the counter and pushed into it with the rolling pin. The dough stuck in ugly strings to the rolling pin and to the counter. Too late, I noticed the sentence about sprinkling flour on the counter and the rolling pin.

Angie wandered into the kitchen as I scraped the dough off the counter and the rolling pin and my hands.

"I hope you don't expect me to eat this pie," she said. "You want to go get a pizza? Dad says he'll take us. And then we're going to get kitten stuff."

"Not now."

"Suit yourself. You can watch Panda while we're gone."

"I'm busy." I'd asked for a kitten until I was nine and then gave up. I couldn't be expected to care about Angie's kitten now. Angie brought the apple basket bed into the kitchen. The kitten slept on a folded purple towel, her paws folded daintily under her fuzzy body.

I skipped down to the directions for the pie filling. The apples had to be peeled. On some TV show once I saw a man peel an apple all in one smooth motion. The curled peel stood on the table like a coiled spring. I imagined apple coils lined neatly along the counter, but my peels came in chunks and my apples had craters, small moons in a line by the bowl.

Joanne shuffled into the kitchen wearing her brown corduroy robe, even though it was the middle of summer. The sleeves hung limp over her hands.

"I said I'd make the pie." She looked at the kitchen from under her eyebrows.

"I wanted to do it myself."

"You're messing up the kitchen. Give me the knife."

I wanted to use it to slash into my real life that waited for me somewhere else, but instead I slapped the knife down on the counter. "I'm going to watch."

She barely looked at me while she finished peeling the apples, but she didn't tell me to get out. I sat at the kitchen table beside Panda's basket. The kitten slept on her back now, one paw covering her eyes. Joanne sliced the apples and set them to boil in a mixture of cinnamon, sugar and water. She poked at my lump of dough in the bowl. "This is useless."

"You didn't let me finish it."

"Pie crusts take practice."

"You won't *let* me practice."

She looked at me as if she hadn't ever seen me before. "Watch me this time." She showed me how the butter and water must be cold, how to use two knives to cut the butter into the flour. Her voice was hoarse. In the time it had taken me to locate the mixing bowl, her crust sat neatly fluted in the pie tin as the filling simmered in its pan.

"You can clean this mess up," she said when the pie had been offered to its oven womb. She sat down at the table across from me and ran her sleeve across her forehead. "It's too hot to be baking." *Take off the robe,* I thought, but I didn't say it.

I washed all the dishes by hand, to make it last, and wiped dough off the cabinet doors and the sink counters. I swirled the mop over the floor, bumping Panda's basket. The kitten jerked awake and demanded dinner in a tiny mew. I poured a splash of milk into a chipped bowl from the set of flowered dishes Joanne had gotten for a wedding present.

Dad and Angie banged through the door while Panda lapped her milk.

"You were supposed to wait for the cat food," said Angie.

"Where's the pizza?" I decided to go off my diet just this one night.

"We ate it there." She caught my look and said, "You said you weren't hungry, and Joanne was asleep." Panda had finished her milk and begun her bath, carefully wetting her paws with her tongue and rubbing her face.

"She's a dignified little thing, isn't she?" Joanne said. She offered her forefinger to Panda, who grabbed the finger with her paws, rolled on her back, and pumped furiously with her back legs on Joanne's hand. Joanne smiled. The oven timer buzzed and I peeked through the window in the oven door. "You and I'll have pie for dinner," she said to me.

We put ice cream on the pie to cool it, and took our plates to the living room to watch TV while we ate. The ice cream melted into a snowy sauce and dripped off our plates. Dad watched us from his lounger, where he had been flipping through the channels. He watched Joanne as if he were trying to memorize dance steps to do later.

Joanne set her pie on the coffee table. Panda perched on her shoulder like a fur ornament while she studied the TV listings.

"Here's a show about pandas."

"Karma," said Angie.

Joanne didn't move through the whole show. The ice cream from her pie dribbled onto the coffee table and she didn't notice. The kitten fell asleep, her face buried in Joanne's robe. When the show ended, Joanne sighed and gently lifted the kitten off her shoulder. She handed her to Angie and went up to bed. Dad kept his eyes on the upstairs landing long after she had disappeared. I thought about the pandas, how they live in smaller and smaller parts of China and ate nothing but bamboo. I didn't see how they could possibly survive. I imagined God giving out tests, saying, "Here are the pandas. Keep them alive, and you're okay." Like balancing a raw egg on a stick. Splat.

"Your mother married me because of green peppers," Dad said, as if someone had asked him. He was still watching the staircase. "She never met a man who knew what they were until she met me. She was seventeen, and her family lived on steak and baked potatoes. They thought that was cooking." He shifted in his chair. "I taught her to cook."

"Will you teach us?"

He ignored me. "We reached for the same pepper at the grocery store at the same time. Now she won't let me in the kitchen."

"Is she sick?" When Angie said it, I realized I'd been wondering the same thing.

But Dad didn't answer. He hadn't been talking to us. "We danced, every night. I taught her to waltz, too." I imagined my parents, young and slim, silhouetted on a far horizon. Joanne's skirts swished around her legs as they danced away, spinning to the music. The colors in the living room altered and I imagined one of those old-time pictures, yellow and grainy.

Angie stroked the motherless kitten. I wondered if Panda had forgotten her mother, or did she think she would see her again? An old comedy came on the TV, one we'd all seen four times before. We sat motionless in the blue light, lumps of butter waiting for someone's hands to bind us together.

Contrapuntal Verses
Robert Eastwood

When her turn has come
she rises, steadies herself,
looks quizzically around the room
of scattered tables, polyglot faces.
Someone hands her horned spectacles.
She shuffles, as the old will do,
not sure the floor would fall away.
Her fingers, like twisted roots,
clutch a small scrawled tablet
she settles slowly in the chair to read.
Her sound has a sprung resonance,
as if forced through disparate reeds.
She reads earnestly, never looking up,
of little flowers that thrived on love,
and sweethearts under April moons.
The cadence marches along,
the rhymes stop abruptly
in the places she stations them.
As she finishes each poem
she flips a page, goes on to the next,
not pausing at the polite applause.
She could hardly hear them anyway.
Her own, girlish voice
is in her ear.

A Prayer for Dad
Katie Tully

I breathed today for the first time in months. I never thought I was morbid, but that's what Aunt Sue said.

"Pray for him. Pray that he'll live," she said and straightened her blouse.

I never thought that praying was useless until that day. Even I, the small, ten-year-old in the corner, knew that Dad wasn't going to get better. Still, every night Aunt Sue came in and prayed with me. *"Our Father who art in Heaven..."* I hated it. I was talking to my hands and telling them to make my Dad better. They couldn't do anything. God couldn't do anything. *"Hallowed be thy name..."* Of course I wanted my Dad to get better, but the cancer was too advanced now. *"Thy kingdom come, Thy will be done..."* So I ate my tears. I didn't cry to anyone but my bedspread. Mom died. Now Dad, then me. I planned my own death. *"On Earth as it is in Heaven..."* Aunt Sue let me leave school. The stares bit into me until I hid in bed, swearing I had cancer, too, and couldn't go to school. *"Give us this day our daily bread..."* Aunt Sue is smart. She pulled me out. She makes me read everyday, to keep up. She hates math, so I don't have to do any. *"Forgive us our trespasses..."* So, today I went to the hospital and Dad told me for the 80th time that today was the last time I would talk to him. *"As we forgive those who trespass against us..."* He says this every time I visit. I always believe him, too, for this is the field of dying (and God). I wished today would be the last time. *"Lead us not into temptation..."* Dad smiled at me, but I winced when I saw his yellow teeth. *Where is his toothbrush?* He held my hand as tightly as he could. A red light on one of the monitors blinked and beeped. Three doctors rushed in. *"But deliver us from evil..."* They pushed me aside. All I could hear was the awful whine of the machine and someone say, "Too late." They fled the room. They smelled death. I smelled Dad. A green line ran across the screen. I hugged him and gasped for air. I finally let him see me cry. *"Amen..."*

The Sabbath Ritual
Bonnie Nish

I'd forgotten the smell of chickens
sawdust beneath their feet
clucking wildly for attention
in mesh cages barely big enough to contain
their plump forms.
Fridays before the heat became unbearable
we rode the crowded streetcar,
my Bubbie and I, holding hands, never speaking
arrived at the open air market.
Old men stooped on corners, uttering the foreign sounds
    of guttural Yiddish
bearded mouths imparting hidden meanings, words, tales,
I had heard only in my Bubbie's house.
The pungent smell of the cheese shop as we crossed the
    street
made me slightly sick,
Crowds of people smacked shoulders
as they passed, tipping black hats
rubbing fingers over ripe fruit
hugging Challah to their breasts
standing in line outside the butcher's shop
the most important stop of the day.
Sometimes I could choose the chicken, a happy one
watching with pride as the butcher carried him to the back
unaware the parcel my grandmother carried out
was our Sabbath dinner.

Her long fingers, blackened by newsprint,
the fingers I loved to squeeze, squeezed mine
as we walked back to the streetcar stop for the journey
    home,
those fingers spoke so many pacts we had silently made
passing traditions from this generation to that without
    ever a word,
passing the heavy parcel from lap to lap, watching
    silently for our stop.
Doors closing behind us we would always linger,
    just for a moment,
pretending to shift the burden of our evening's meal
    from hip to hip
as we listened for the whispering prayers of swaying trees.
A warm wind blowing graciously across her aging face,
    enough time coveted
my grandmother entered the house with a smile
    and one tear.

Shop Lucky 24 Hours
Camille DeFer Thompson

Safeway was closed. The banner across the front of the store announced, OPEN 24 HOURS. But it was closed. A few vehicles dotted the parking lot. As Melanie drove past the entrance, she noticed an employee's head poked out of the half-open automatic door, talking to a customer. A crude cardboard sign hanging on the door read, "CLOSED — POWER FAILURE."

Shit. 11:38 on Sunday night and Safeway was closed. She U-turned and headed out of the parking lot. Lucky was a mile away. She hated Lucky's cold cuts. Admittedly, she had never knowingly eaten them to make a fair judgment. She was sure she must hate them because her mother always hated Lucky's cold cuts.

But she had no choice. The luncheon meeting was tomorrow and she was assigned to bring the cold cuts. The next nearest Safeway was three exits down the freeway. With an 8:00 meeting in Oakland in the morning she couldn't stop on the way in. She was destined for Lucky's deli meats.

I hate Lucky's cold cuts, Melanie repeated to herself as she surveyed the remains of the salads, hoping for inspiration. This had to be the un-Luckiest night of her life.

"Me, too."

Melanie started at the words, then turned in the direction they had come from and the wheelchair that had pulled up beside her. The occupant's blue eyes twinkled up at her as his hand swept at a tangle of thick wavy black hair stubbornly tumbling to his forehead. Suddenly aware of her dyed shade 8A locks hurriedly pulled into a ponytail before she left the house, she hoped her dark roots weren't too noticeable. The at-home dye job had been a disaster. Deciding she needed a change after her last boyfriend dumped her for a blonde, she had acted on a whim. Foolish. And so unlike her. She vowed never to behave so impulsively again.

"Excuse me?" Melanie's words sounded more terse to her than she had intended. Softening, she continued. "'You, too,' what?"

"Your remark about Lucky's deli meats," the stranger replied. "I agree."

"Oh! Did I say that out loud?" Feeling her neck and face warm with embarrassment, she wondered if the counter clerk had heard her, too.

Seeming not to notice, the man continued. "I know a great deli in Walnut Creek. I get all my cold cuts there."

Melanie forced a polite smile. "That's not going to help me now. I need something tonight. Thanks anyway."

She began to discreetly move away. Charmed though she was, not to mention flattered, by this attractive man's insistence upon keeping her engaged, still, she told herself, it was too late for a sojourn to Walnut Creek for cold cuts.

Undeterred, the man said, "No problem. They're open all night."

"You're kidding," Melanie said, her curiosity now aroused. "I thought all night delis only existed in Seinfeld and movies about New York."

"It's a fifteen minute drive, tops. You can follow me."

Here it comes, Melanie thought. The middle of the night, a helpless, desperate woman in need of deli products. Coincidentally, this all night deli would be right around the corner from his place. But hey, why not a drink first? No. No way was she falling for this one. Did he think she had been living under a rock for

the last ten years? This had to be the sorriest pickup
attempt she had ever been a party to.

"No. I... I don't..." She stumbled over the
rejection. Why the hesitation? He wasn't that
charming. And even if he was, it was the middle of the
night, for Pete's sake. She wasn't stupid.

"No problem." His understanding half-smile was a
relief. "I'll give you directions. It's easy to find."

"No. I didn't mean that. I mean... that I don't trust
you... I mean..." This was not going well. Make up
your mind, Melanie, she admonished herself. Then she
remembered the promise she had made to herself never
to be impulsive again. That decided it.

His eyes lost their sparkle and turned down to the
floor. "I understand. Forget it. I just thought you
looked a little desperate. Sorry."

"No. I mean... yes. I am desperate... about the cold
cuts, I mean."

The twinkle returned to his eyes and a smile spread
across his face. "Great. I'm in the burgundy van out
front. Flash your lights when you're behind me. By the
way, what's your name?"

"Uh... Melanie."

"Pleased to meet you, Uhmelanie. I'm Frank." He
smiled and extended his left hand. Expecting his right
hand, then noticing it for the first time resting in his lap
fingers bent and atrophied, she fumbled a moment, then
finally grasped his good hand in an awkward handshake.

"I'm... sorry... I mean..." Geez, she thought. If I
don't calm down, he'll think I can't complete a
sentence.

A cloud of vulnerability darkened his face for a
moment. "Forget it. Happens all the time."

She listened intently to the directions he offered as
backup in case they got separated along the way. So
much for the vow of prudence.

"Give me a minute when I get in the van. I've got
to call my wife and tell her I'll be late. She worries if

I'm out when she gets home from work. She's a nurse at Valley Med Center. Works midnights."

Melanie felt her face flush again. Wife? If he was trying to pick me up would he so blatantly announce that he was married? Maybe he really was just a sincere guy out to help a woman in distress. Or was that just part of his scheme?

The night was clear, the moon full, as she tooled down the freeway in her quest for deli goods. After the promised fifteen minutes, Melanie pulled into the parking lot of the strip mall. Grateful for the directions she had been given, having lost her guide somewhere on 680, she waited in the car for a few minutes. She had decided that if there was no open deli at their destination, she would just turn around and head back to Lucky. If he followed her, she'd call the police from her cell phone.

But in fact, there was a deli—and it appeared to be open. All the storefronts were dark except for the deli. Squinting against the light coming from the window, she made out the figure of a man in a white butcher's apron moving through the aisles. Remarkable, she thought. An all night deli in California. Feeling increasingly nervous sitting alone in the deserted parking lot, she decided to wait for Frank inside. As she pulled open the door to the shop, she noticed the sticker displaying the store hours. Mon.-Fri. 7:00 a.m.-7:00 p.m., Sat. & Sun., 9:00 a.m.-7:00 p.m. Odd. If it's an all night deli, why is there a posted closing time?

Responding to the bell announcing her entrance, the man in the apron turned to face her.

She let out an audible gasp when she looked into an identical set of twinkling blue eyes and tangle of black hair.

"Wh-what is going on? My God, you're twins."

Bewilderment spread across the shop owner's face. "Excuse me? Is there something I can help you with?"

Struggling to regain her composure, Melanie replied, "I'm sorry. Your brother should be here soon. I met him at Lucky and he said I should come here and try your cold cuts. Well, it all sounds a little silly now, but at the time it seemed like a good idea. You see, I need cold cuts for an office luncheon tomorrow and. . ."

The man in the apron interrupted her blubbering monologue.

"Did you say 'brother?' My brother brought you here?"

"Well, I assume he's your brother. He looks exactly like you."

His face paled. He turned away then in a moment, looked back at her.

"Ma'am. I'm sure you're mistaken. I don't have a brother."

His sharp tone surprised Melanie. Confused and embarrassed, she reached for the door. "I'm sorry. I... It's just that I met a man at Lucky's in San Ramon and he gave me directions here. Said he'd meet me here. He looked so much like you I thought he must be your brother." Shaking her head, she continued. "This was a bad idea. I need to get out of here."

The man touched her shoulder. "No, wait. It's not your fault. They say everyone has a twin somewhere in the world. My name's Craig. Can I get something for you?"

This was too weird. Even the two men's voices sounded alike. She just wanted out of there. But then she remembered the luncheon meeting tomorrow. And after all, this was a deli and she did need cold cuts. She was suddenly aware of the delicious mixture of scents around her.

Extending a trembling hand, she said, "I'm Melanie." Craig's grip was firm, confident, so different from an earlier handshake, she recalled sadly.

"How can I help you?"

She explained her dilemma and he suggested some cuts of meat.

As he rang up her purchases, he said, "Well, I guess your mystery guide isn't going to show. Listen, tell me if I'm out of line, but are you free for dinner sometime?"

This was not happening. First she strolls in after business hours, rattles off some lame story about meeting his twin brother who doesn't exist, the guy, whoever he is, doesn't show up to corroborate her story, then the deli owner asks her out. She was beginning to wonder where the candid camera was hidden.

"I'm flattered, really. But, this whole night has been too bizarre. I... I just don't think it would be a good idea."

Craig handed her purchases across the counter. "I can't say I blame you. But I just had to ask. You've got a great smile. Hey, be sure to let me know how the cold cuts go over, huh."

"Sure. You know, something has been bothering me since I walked in here. I noticed your store hours on the door as I came in. Don't you close at 7:00 on Sundays?"

"Yeah. I was in bed, had just dozed off when the phone rang. It went dead as soon as I picked it up. Must've been a wrong number. Anyway, I couldn't get back to sleep. I only live a couple blocks from here, so I decided to come in. There's always something to do. What a coincidence, huh?"

"Yeah, a coincidence," Melanie repeated, not quite convinced. "But the door was unlocked."

Craig's forehead wrinkled into a frown. "Funny, I don't remember unlocking it. Must've done it without thinking."

Melanie smiled and picked up her package. "Well, thanks again. I'll see you."

Just as she turned toward the door, the bell clanged, announcing another customer.

A young pregnant woman ambled toward them. "Mel, is that you? Ohmygod! I didn't know you shopped here."

It was a co-worker, Stephanie, from sales. She had been off for three weeks on maternity leave, and looked ready to deliver any minute.

"Stephanie! What are you doing here at this hour? Where's Jim?

"Oh, I left him snoring in bed. I got this wild craving for some of Craig's smoked gouda and, well..." She giggled and pointed to her swollen belly.

Turning to Craig, she said, "I looked out the window to see if you were still up. Thought you might have a stash in your fridge. I noticed your truck was gone and figured you had to be here." Then to Melanie, "Craig lives next door to us. Nicest guy you ever want to meet, but he has no life. Home and this place. That's it. So Mel, what are you doing here?"

Melanie glanced at Craig, who had moved to the other side of the shop as soon as the mother-to-be had expressed the object of her craving. "It's a long story, Stephanie. I'll call you tomorrow."

Stephanie looked in the direction of the counter and watched Craig slicing cheese for her. "It's so sad, isn't it? About his brother, I mean. You heard, didn't you?"

Melanie's head tilted with incredulity. "His brother?"

"Yeah. They're twins... or were, well, whatever. Anyway, he died, his brother that is. Like two years ago or so."

Stephanie's forehead wrinkled in thought. "His name was Fred, or something..."

"Frank?" Melanie supplied.

"Yeah, Frank. That's it. So you knew?"

"Lucky guess. Go on."

"Anyway, Frank was a cop. Got shot in the line of duty and it paralyzed him. His testimony put the guy in jail. When the guy got paroled, he murdered Frank. They found him shot to death in his van.

"Craig just about lost it. Stopped hanging with his friends, dating, everything. That's what I meant by 'no life.' Frank's wife even tried to help him. She's a nurse down in Pleasanton, or somewhere. I think she got a shrink friend of hers to talk to him for awhile. I'm always trying to get him out... having him over and stuff. But, he's like a hermit. He's beginning to come out of it, but he's pretty lonely. Still can't even talk about his brother."

Craig returned with a small package and a few slices of cheese on a paper towel which he offered to Stephanie. "I figured that craving wouldn't wait until you got home. Help yourself."

As Stephanie indulged on her treat, Melanie dug into her purse and pulled out a business card. "I've changed my mind. Dinner sounds great," she said, handing the card to Craig.

Stephanie looked at Melanie then Craig, then back at Melanie again. "Dinner? Are you guys going out? This is so cool! Wait 'til I tell Jimmy."

Looking at Melanie smiling up at him, Craig said, "Why the change of heart?"

"Hey," Melanie replied, "Stephanie says you're all right, and I know better than to argue with a pregnant woman."

They all laughed and finished the last of the cheese.

"Now I really have to go," Melanie. "I've got an early meeting tomorrow. Can I drive you home, Steph?"

"Nah. That's all right. It's just a couple of blocks. Craig'll give me a lift, huh?"

Craig smiled and nodded, his cheeks stuffed with cheese.

Melanie walked out to the car and climbed in. As she started the engine and fastened her seatbelt, she looked back toward the deli, and watched the figures of Craig and Stephanie. She had read about people's personal experiences with angels, but she couldn't reconcile it with her own reality. Still struggling to absorb the events of the evening, she turned out of the parking lot and looked down the road. She was sure she caught a glimpse of a burgundy van disappearing in the darkness.

From Ocean to Ocean
Jean Ohman

The silver Indian-Pacific train, pulled out of the Sydney station at precisely 2:55 p.m. We were heading west through Australia, 2,700 miles across this vast country, from Sydney to Perth, from the Pacific to the Indian Ocean. A line in the brochure advertised, "This is one of the longest rail routes in the world, through some of the most inhospitable country on earth."

Sails of the Opera House faded in the distance as we explored our First Class accommodations. "Doesn't look exactly like the brochure," my travel companion, Pat, commented as she peered into our compartment. A bench seat held promise of one lower berth, and we knew from the hooks above that one of us would spend the night in the upper berth, suspended from the rafters. I was sure it would be me. A door led to a tiny room, billed as our *ensuite* bathroom. Two latches, one marked sink, the other toilet, hung from a stainless steel wall. Pulling them down, we found both. A shower fixture above, sprayed water covering our complete *ensuite*.

Walking into the lounge car, Pat whispered, "I thought we would meet interesting people, all I see are a bunch of old fogies." It probably didn't help when I suggested that as two women, with my hair as silver as the train, we must look the same to them. Most of the passengers were Australian. A few had traveled from England, but we seemed to be the only Americans.

The middle-aged group sat on burgundy upholstered chairs scattered throughout the lounge. Various shades of the same color in draperies and carpet added a touch of class, but I found no sign of the expected wood-paneled walls and brass fittings. Not exactly the Orient

Express, I thought to myself. We sat in the glass smoker's bubble that dominated the center of the car. I felt on display, as though in a cocoon of some sort.

A good looking man about our age came in a few minutes later and joined us in lively conversation. Our new friend Peter, a well-traveled Australian, shared his knowledge of the country as our train snaked through the Blue Mountains outside Sydney. I laughed at his quick wit, observed his charming mannerisms, and decided our adventure for the next three days looked a bit brighter.

Peter joined us as we sipped a cold drink from the bar in the lounge, waiting for the dinner call. At seven-thirty we headed for the dining room where Peter's stories of Australia entertained us throughout our meal of pumpkin soup and Salmon Wellington. Our conversation continued until the staff pulled off the maroon table cloths, brought out the vacuum cleaners, and hinted that we adjourn to the lounge.

Over a glass of port, Peter educated us on the proper use of the terms, Aborigines and Aboriginal. "The first is a noun, the second an adjective, "he reminded us. I was surprised when he told us there were only about three hundred thousand Aborigines living in Australia.

"Many more were here before the Europeans arrived," Peter continued. "Thousands died from diseases brought into their land. Others were simply killed or run off to make room for the new arrivals. The Aborigines have lived here forty thousand years, but their way of life drastically changed as new eating habits were introduced, and they were forced into clothing and housing to live as we do. Their spiritual beliefs were challenged when well meaning missionaries tried to impose their religion on the Aboriginal tribes. We still have many problems we need to work through," he concluded, giving us much to think about as we parted company and headed for our sleeping compartments.

The gentle oscillating of the train lulled us to sleep that first night and by the next morning we had adjusted to the confined space. Kangaroos and emus bounced past our window as we waited for breakfast. We watched for signs of life around water holes and soon the hopping movement of kangaroos caught our eyes. The animals moved quickly and blended into the red earth. A few trees, appearing dead, and some scrubby bushes, rose above the powdery soil. The hazy sky and diffused light brought shadows of mutable color and texture to the land.

Shortly after nine o'clock the train pulled into the remote mining town of Broken Hill. We had sadly learned this was Peter's destination and said our good-byes at breakfast while drinking hot coffee and eating our fill of savory omelets and sausages. "Gotta go," Peter said, grabbing his suitcase and promising to see us someday in California. "No worries, mates," he added with a smile, charming us with that typically Australian expression.

A few hours later we pulled into Adelaide for a two hour stop in Australia's fifth largest city. Leaving the train and paying ten Australian dollars each, we boarded a tour bus. Traveling around the city, we listened to the narrative of a driver clearly proud of his home town. Open parks and broad stretches of lush grassland surrounded the clustered skyline of medium sized high rises. "You can do anything you want in our parks, walk your dog, read a book, or play ball, as long as you do no harm. The parks belong to the people," the driver told us several times.

Pat and I got back on the train in time for a pre-dinner drink and a look at what the new passengers coming aboard might bring. "There's a couple that look interesting," Pat said, as she spotted two new faces. They introduced themselves as Rob and Sue, and by the end of our first dinner together we felt like old friends. In fact, a few weeks later we spent three days with them in their home near Melbourne.

Rob and Sue are Australian and, like Peter, shared their knowledge and insights about the country. We talked of the geographical changes since leaving Sydney: rocky canyons in the Blue Mountains, then long flat stretches of differing colors of soil, with only a few kangaroos and emus to break the repetitious landscape. Small hills rolled up in the distance, accentuating the lovely contrast of rusty colored soil and leafy bushes.

As evening fell, harsher colors of the day gave way to soft shades of purple and blue. I wanted to reach through the sealed windows to feel the night air or walk along the shifting dunes to experience the essence of the desert.

It startled me as I looked out the window early the next morning, to see how night winds and dewy moisture transformed the red sand into geometric patterns. I watched silvery clouds line the sky, waiting for the morning sun. Bushes, and the low prickly plant called spinifex, wearing shades of yellow-green and dusty gray, filled the slightly contoured landscape. Some shrubs had turned a bright lemon color, the only sign of autumn in this vast desert. A few gum and mulga trees stood in the distance. Perhaps the last, I thought, for soon we would enter the Nullarbor Plain. The stretch of almost 300 miles is nearly devoid of trees, and is said to be the longest straight railway track in the world.

The flat land became hypnotic. I wondered how the engineer could stay awake. A passenger told me that the engineer had to push a button every ninety seconds or the train's brakes were automatically applied, and that it takes one and one half miles for the train to stop.

Tracks from a large vehicle ran along the side the train, a sign that people were near. A wind-sock and small landing strip in the distance confirmed my guess. A few shed-like buildings appeared, reflecting sunlight on aluminum sides and roofs. We were near the town of Ooldea, and I thought it might be the Aboriginal settlement where the English woman, Daisy Bates, lived and wrote for so many years, earlier this century.

The land was now flat for as far as I could see, much as Daisy Bates described from her small tent lost in this vastness. I tried to imagine being isolated as she was for months at a time, waiting for her Aboriginal friends to come to her for medical help, food or comfort. Kabbarli, they called her, their term for grandmother. She tried to keep their culture from changing, perhaps even being destroyed by the European influence—the intrusion of clothing, unfamiliar foods and religious beliefs.

We passed the Ooldea settlement during breakfast and started the long ride across the Nullarbor. The scene changed almost instantly as mulga, gum and desert oak trees disappeared. Only a few low clusters of greenish-gray vegetation—mostly spinifex, remained. Tan colored rocks suddenly appeared in abundance. They were scattered near the surface, uncovered by the shifting of powdery soil. It was a peculiar sight and I wondered about their existence on this desert plain that seemed as distant and remote as the moon's surface.

Mid-morning we pulled into a siding called Cook for a half-hour stop to refuel and take on water. Once home to around fifty people, only three live there now as the town nears extinction. It once served the railroad, taking care of repairs by providing machinery and manpower. New technology minimized the need for maintenance and people became unnecessary. Concrete *sleepers,* designed to last fifty years, have replaced traditional wooden cross-ties now piled in heaps along the track. Perhaps the old ties will become firewood if there is anyone left to look for heat during the cool nights.

It's strange to imagine people living here for any length of time, but for those who did, it must have been hard to give up this unusual way of life. The people have drifted away looking for another siding or changing their lives in ways they may not choose. Like the wooden ties, the people have become remnants of the past, symbols of days when life was harsh, yet uncomplicated. They lived in a safe place where neighbors formed extended families, taking care of each other and sharing their lives in ways impossible to imagine in a large city.

Large rain catchers sat outside small wood-framed and aluminum-roofed houses. A building marked "Office," a school, two old jail cells and an assortment of utility buildings, made up the rest of the town. A swimming pool, now filled with sand, remains in the common area. Six hundred stunted trees, donated and planted by volunteers from Adelaide and Perth years ago, now serve as memories of people shielded from the outside world. It's an isolated place where ants and flies now rule.

As we passed Rawlinna, near the western edge of the Nullarbor Plain, the landscape changed again. Trees reappeared on the horizon. Some had clusters of leaves on top of long spindly trunks and branches, like stalks of old broccoli or tethered balloons. Silky white gum trees stood in the distance. Australians call them Ghost gums, because they appear like lost spirits during dusky nights.

We watched a group of emus stroll across the land, but kangaroos did not come into view for some distance. As the brush increased, the animals hid and found refuge from the heat. Occasionally a small maintenance shed appeared with a water tank or signs of a telephone line. Sometimes we saw a house or two nearby and a dirt road going off in the distance, to what seemed like nowhere.

The sky began to darken and I waited for the red sunset I had hoped to see. A few slivers of red lined the desert sky, but even they disappeared quickly as we slid into night. The sky became black and layers of thin clouds covered hidden stars.

The train stopped for two hours in the town of Kalgoorlie, three hundred seventy miles east of Perth. We joined a bus tour and spent forty-five minutes learning about this historic city of thirty thousand people. Prospectors found gold here in 1893 and it's referred to as the Golden Mile. "The richest square mile of gold-bearing earth in the world," our guide told us. By 1903, a three hundred fifty mile pipeline brought water, allowing the development of hotels and attractive buildings that remain there today.

An enormous pit leads to miles of underground roads and tunnels where gold is still found in quantities large enough for the town's survival. Our guide described the town as "a bit rough," showing us a place called Hay Street. Outside small flat-roofed buildings, local prostitutes in black mesh stockings waited for customers. They waved as we passed by.

The train bounced roughly on the tracks during the final stretch of our trip. More than once at night, I wondered what it would be like to fall from my perch near the roof of the train. My narrow bed had no guard rail, and a miscalculated turn could tumble me to the floor.

Time went by quickly and the scenery some described as boring never materialized, at least not for me. Seeing a country like Australia—from east to west—was to feel the magic of new frontiers waiting to be conquered. It's a county with people made strong by the harshness of the land, facing challenges such as those found in America one hundred years ago.

Early on our last morning the compact skyline of Perth came into view. Lights of the city became visible as we watched the desert fade in the distance. At seven o'clock we pulled into the station, exchanging a land locked in the past for the pace of a large modern city. I didn't want the adventure to end and felt a little sadness as we gathered our belongings, said goodbye to our new friends, and stepped off the train.

Our journey from ocean to ocean had been a journey through time. It took sixty-four hours. I would do it again in a minute.

Union Park, Carrick Knowe
Robert Eastwood

The dawn brightens. The park a dense foot in mist,
gauze wisps, fluttering with jabbering gulls---
brackish Edinburgh. No brash pipes as I run

here, skimming worm lairs, wounding grass, a run
through stench of tar, pitch-pot whorling in mist,
billowing across the park with braying gulls.

Wizened men in tweed, pancake hats, note the gulls
and me as they puff fags, intersect my run---
silent heads down, walking in to hollow mist.

Mist gulls me. Wings me in my run amidst gulls.

Pio

Margaret Roemer

Pio would start working early in the morning when the town's merchants would be rolling down their canvas awnings in front of their stores. Even at that early hour, Main Street would be bustling with horse-driven carriages, wagons, carts, and buggies. The clatter of horses' hoofs, squeaky wagon wheels, and the drivers' loud commands would resonate down Main Street. The drivers drove with reckless abandon. They turned their horses on a moment's notice, and they would speed up their horses to dash wildly down the street. A pedestrian would risk life and limb attempting to cross the street during the chaotic morning traffic. Rather than being trampled by a horse, or run over by a wagon, nobody crossed the street.

The dust churned up in the air by the wheels of the wagons and the horses' hoofs caused a veritable dust storm that hovered all the way down Main Street. It was for this reason that most women would come to town in the afternoon to shop; when the wagons had left and the dust had settled.

Pio's job in the morning was to sweep the wood plank sidewalks in front of the merchants' stores. He used a large straw broom, and the sweeping was tedious. It would be noon before he was finished sweeping both sides of Main Street. He would then find a shady tree and unfold a piece of cloth that held his lunch, which was a tortilla filled with refried beans. When he was finished eating, he would then lean against the tree with his back and close his eyes for a "siesta."

Awakening an hour later, he would walk down to the fire station on the other end of Main Street, and take a large wooden wheelbarrow out of a small shed. A large shovel and a square stiff broom hung from hooks on both sides of the wheelbarrow. Starting from one end of Main Street, he would pick up the "roadapples" or "calling cards" that had been deposited by the horses during the morning with the shovel. When the wheelbarrow was full, he would take the load of horse manure and dump it on the field behind the fire station. Anyone caught downwind from the full cart of manure would get a repugnant scent. It was overpowering. Children passing would yell out, "peeyew!" Pio would smile and wave to the children. He was eventually tagged by that name by everyone in town. The grownups thought it was his given name, but it wasn't. Pio's Indian given name was "Two Toes."

When Pio was only a month old, his mother left him in the teepee while she went to gather roots, greens, and acorns for the evening meal. When she returned, she found a large rat gnawing on the toes of her baby. She killed the rat. Only the large and small toe remained on the baby's right foot. The shaman in the Indian camp nodded in approval as Pio's mother brought the rat she had skinned and roasted for his evening meal. He told her that the baby's name would be "Two Toes," and that he would eat the rat and then come to her tent for the baby's healing ritual. Small babies bitten by rats usually die, but Pio survived.

At sundown, after Pio had dumped the last load in back of the fire station, he headed for his one-room wooden shanty five blacks north of town . Pio was thankful for the thirty dollars he received each month as the town's sweeper. It was better than working as a farm hand fourteen hours a day. He was not supervised; he was his own boss. He could work at his own pace; nobody gave him orders. It gave him a good independent feeling. He planned to save as much money as he could in order to buy a few acres and own a horse.

Arriving at his shanty, he removed his shoes which were permeated with the odor of horse dung, and left them outside. He brought in a pail of water that had been warmed by the afternoon sun. He removed his work clothes and hung them on a large hook protruding from the wall. He dipped a washcloth in the pail of warm water and washed his body. He then bent over the pail and washed his hair. He dried himself and then sat on the edge of his bed soaking his feet until the warm water turned cold. He covered himself with a hand-woven blanket that his grandmother had made for him when he was small. He remembered watching her patiently weaving the intricate pattern, her forehead creased in concentration. Whenever she looked up and saw him staring at her, she would give him a wide toothless smile, gather him up, and press him against the soft folds of her round body. Still thinking about his grandmother, he closed his eyes. He was soon fast asleep.

He would awaken exactly two hours later and grope for the box of matches in the darkness. He struck a match and lit the wick of the kerosene lamp which glowed immediately lighting up the one room shanty. He got up and began dressing. A purple satin shirt he had purchased from the gypsy caravan, soft leather pants, and a matching jacket completed his outfit. He stuffed a clean handkerchief in a moccasin, tried it on, then took it off to rearrange the handkerchief until his foot was comfortable. The handkerchief filled the space between the two toes on his right foot. He combed his shoulder length black hair. He was ready to leave.

He picked up the kerosene lamp and the box of matches and placed them just outside the door of his shanty. He closed the door and lowered the wick of the lamp until the light was smothered. He stood still a few moments until his eyes adjusted to the darkness, then began to walk towards the Prince Bismark Saloon.

As he approached the saloon, he could hear the fiery
Mexican band playing a peppery tune. The laughter of
the men inside rose above the music. He swallowed
hard. His throat was dry. He fingered the ten-cent
coin in his hand. It was the amount he allowed himself
for beer each day. His empty stomach began to make
large growling noises as he entered the saloon.

He went directly to the bar of the Prince Bismark
Saloon where the customary free lunch platters were
heaped with food. Salami, cheese, Portuguese
Linguica, hard-boiled eggs, and slices of fresh
homemade bread made his mouth water. He sat within
reach of the platters and placed the ten-cent piece on
the bar in front of him. Two foaming glasses of beer
were immediately placed before him. He took a huge
gulp of beer and then helped himself to the food. He
didn't speak to anyone until he was finished eating.
Stomach full, he gazed at the remaining almost empty
glass of beer in front of him. He turned his attention to
the man seated next to him, and began to engage him in
a conversation. Pio was an innovative and gifted story
teller. Once he began a story, both men seated on
either side of him became avid listeners. By the time
Pio came to the crucial part of his story, his two beer
glasses were empty.

Pio became mute. He licked his lips, and stared at
his empty beer glasses. The two men patiently waited
for Pio to continue his story. Not one word passed his
lips. It became evident to both men that Pio's lips
would remain glued shut until a beer was placed before
him. The two men anxious to hear the rest of the story,
each placed five cents on the bar in front of Pio and
yelled to the bartender, "Bring Pio here two beers. His
well has run dry. Ha! Ha!"

The bartender brought two glasses of beer and
placed them in front of Pio, who lifted one glass to his
lips and took a few gulps. The beer loosened his
tongue; he resumed his story, which became more

exciting as the evening wore on. The two men fueled Pio with more glasses of beer as Pio's story continued to titillate them throughout the evening.

Much later, the lights were dimmed in the saloon. It was a warning message that the saloon would close in ten minutes. This signaled the band to play the grand finale song with much vitality. Pio hopped off his bar stool and announced to the two men that he would continue his story the next night, since there wasn't enough time to finish it. He then began to dance to the lively music, twirling his body, kicking up his heels, and stomping his feet to the beat of the music.

"O'l Pio's doin' his war dance," shouted the two men as they clapped their hands to the music and joined him dancing.

Soon everyone in the saloon began stomping their cowboy boots to the rhythm of the pulsating music. When the music ended, Pio was gone. He had quietly slipped out and vanished into the darkness.

When the buggies, carts, and carriages were replaced by Model-T Fords, Main Street's dirt road was paved with asphalt, and the wooden plank sidewalks were replaced by concrete sidewalks. But, by that time, Pio had diligently saved his money and was able to buy ten acres and a magnificent Appaloosa horse which he proudly road bareback, Indian style, in the Rodeo Parades. He raced his appaloosa on Sunday afternoons and won enough money, in one year, to last him for the rest of his life. He could then afford to buy more than two beers, but he never did.

Opening Night
Naomi Forrest

Through the stage door
Into the dressing room.
Rustling, rumbling and chattering
With a stomach full of butterflies.
Five minutes!

From black and white to cosmetic colors.
Masking to look like something else.
Costumes, props, and additional lines
With a piggyback of fear.
Three minutes!

Backstage with everyone
To participate in confusion.
Final tips, smiles and a mouse's "Shhhh."
With a final prayer disguised as a four-leaf clover.
One minute!

Behind the curtain
Feeling the lights dim.
A statue in silence and hearing but one single breath
With excitement to numb the pressure.
Standing in the spotlight.

Fish Have No Voices
Steve Hellman

Three years Aaron hadn't seen his dad and now his dad was coming all the way down from Montana to pick him up, to take him back up there to go fishing. Aaron couldn't believe, he kept telling his friends, "Fishing, it's what my dad does best. He's the greatest." He stayed up late, so full of thinking about the tall man he remembered, big-handed, sure, he couldn't even sleep. Aaron's mother told him, "You'll want to be careful around your dad, be polite. He takes his fishing seriously. You don't want to argue with him."

By the time his dad arrived at their house in Los Angeles, Aaron didn't know what to believe. The man who pulled up in the driveway, he stepped out of the pickup truck in this long sleeved shirt, with a dark beard. No sooner did his dad jump up the steps, he yelled to Aaron real loud, "Hello!"

It backed Aaron up into his mother's hands. His mom wouldn't let go of him and she got quiet. But then his dad had a gift for him, a black-handled knife, brand new, big in his father's hand.

"You'll need this for fishing, son."

Aaron's mom said, "Are you sure he should have that thing?"

"Oh mom, sure I should, sure I should."

He took the knife from his dad, and then Aaron's mom and his dad had to have a moment alone together, in the house. Aaron opened its blade. It flicked out shiny and pointed, and flicked back in. The knife was cool, with a little deer carved in its black handle. He squared his shoulders and took in a deep breath, seeing himself with his knife.

On the ride up to Montana, they stayed overnight in Nevada, at a motel. There his dad brought out all the gear he had bought new, the champagne of poles and Mitchell-Garcia reels and gnarly-looking hooks. He displayed everything for Aaron in considerable detail, his dad saying they were going to have a hell of a great time, despite what his mom might think.

"Your mom's been mouthing on me, hasn't she?"

"No, not really," Aaron said. He asked what the knife was for.

His dad said in that loud voice, "For gutting fish, goddamn son. Of course, what else?"

Aaron slid the knife in his pocket and looked down, hoping they wouldn't catch a fish they had to gut.

They got up to Montana, to Dillon, over by the Beaverhead River, and then on to his father's favorite spot, the Big Hole River. The river ran from riffle to deep pool, in curves between its sandy banks and rocks, the water smelling strongly of willows thick along the banks, almost too thick to climb through. Moss drying on the small, round stones along the water made walking slippery. From the edge of the river, Aaron saw the water circling into a deep pool, the whole river surface seeming to churn slowly.

Mosquitoes were thick in the air like whining clouds he had to bat constantly from his face.

He couldn't wait to get his hook in the water while his father rigged their poles and outfits. His father said a rainbow fought for its life once you hooked it, like the dickens, so they had to keep a constant grip on their poles or the fish would yank the pole and the reel, and the boy into the river.

"Couldn't have that now, could we. What would your mama think?"

Aaron watched his dad pinch a blood-red worm onto his hook, and then he made Aaron do the same. He winced, squeezing the wiggly body clear past the barb.

The pool flowed deep from the shoal of round smooth river stones that stretched above into a rippling rapids. After his father showed him how to cast, they both cast out into the riffle, letting their lines tread down into the pool. His dad got the first bite. His pole bent in the sunlight, and he started reeling in hard, the line dancing in the river, clear glistening pearls of water flying off it.

His dad flipped the trout out onto the rocks, and the brilliance flashed in the sunlight, flapping and jumping around until Aaron slapped his hands down on it, a gleaming trout, its tail twitching fierce against his hands. He cried for his dad to come help him and his dad came over, lifting the fish by the line. His father stuck his fingers inside its mouth and got at the hook.

"Damn," his dad said, *"teeth!"*

The fish's mouth gaped open, soundless with its red gills flaring.

"Don't hurt it," Aaron said.

His father yanked out the hook, with the fish making a small, squeaking sound like it was being squashed too tight in his father's hands.

"You're hurting it," Aaron said.

"It's what you do," his father said. "It's going to be shouting time, oh boy, will it ever." He swung the fish against a rock, in a motion like a hatchet, bashing its head. The green, speckled trout made another squeezing sound.

"Throw it back in the water," Aaron said.

His father bashed its head against the rock again. Aaron grabbed his dad's arm.

"Son," his father said, "it's what you do. You kill it so it won't suffer, and then you gut it."

Aaron stared at the fish, wondering what it must feel.

"Where's your knife, son?"

Aaron felt the black-handled knife in his pocket, folded up thick and heavy against his thigh. He lifted it out and his father made him open it.

"How come it doesn't cry out, or make some other sound?"

His father cradled the fish belly-up in his palm, and stuck the sharp tip of the blade into it. He sliced clean up through the soft, silver underside, the trout emitting a gurgling noise. The guts came out in a clump, orange and pink, sliding between his father's fingers, and then he jerked them loose and tossed them out where they splashed into the lazy-flowing pool.

"They haven't got voices," Aaron said. "Fish haven't got a way to cry out."

It came to him as simple as that, and Aaron wanted to tell his father he didn't like fishing any more. He wanted to tell him it was useless fun, if you had to kill the fish, for what, to eat it? He'd rather eat a hamburger, or a vegetable. He'd even eat broccoli before he'd want to kill a fish, just to eat it.

But he didn't say any of this, seeing the look on his father's face. Only he went back to his pole, lifting up the line with the blood-dark worm on the hook. He didn't want to disappoint his father, because his father had gone to all this trouble, buying the equipment and bringing him up here. Not knowing what else to do, Aaron cast out into the same pool, vaguely hoping there weren't another fish for miles around stupid enough to take the worm.

Suddenly he felt a tug on his line like something wanted to take the pole from him. He jumped back, holding onto the jerking pole, the line taut, pulling like crazy in the water, zigzagging. The air around him went quiet, only a soft, distant sound like laughing from the splashing water.

His father's voice broke through the calm. "Reel it in, for godsakes, son! You got a big one."

Aaron reeled in and the pole jerked furiously back and forth in his hands. He yanked on the pole, thinking what he must have on the line was something so alive and big, it would never want to come out and die. The trout sailed out of the water, into an arc over the pool, a glittering rainbow, twirling and jerking in midair before it splashed back down into the water, fighting the whole way. Aaron stood there dumbstruck. He didn't know what else to do. If he let go of the pole, if he let the fish get away, his father would be furious.

"My God!" His father burst out at him, "Reel it in, reel it in." Almost snatching the pole from his hands. But Aaron held on. It was one big fish, it came into the shallows, thick and strong, flapping in the rocks. It had a spotted green back Aaron could see smashing at the shallow water. His father splashed out into the river up to his shins, grabbing the fish, lifting the amazing trout out of the water, like it were *his.*

Aaron hated his father for what he was about to do, with his fish. The trout was strong, its body thick and flapping in his father's big hands. And even as his father cursed and pulled at the hook buried in its mouth, Aaron knew the fish wasn't going to die. Because when his father got the hook out, and he was about to hit its head on a rock, before it made that squeaky sound and had its belly slit, Aaron let go of the pole.

It banged onto the rocks at his feet.

"Let it go," he said.

His father looked up, "Good God, son."

Aaron backed up and couldn't believe his father would actually want to kill a fish that beautiful.

"It's not your fish, let it go."

"What in hell's got into you?"

"I said let it go, dad." His voice rising. "I said let it go, because it hasn't got a voice, and I'm telling you, let it go!"

"For godsakes, son. You don't let a fish this size go."

"LET IT GO!"

And with that, Aaron stomped on the fishing pole, felt it snap underfoot, stomped on it again, smashing it and the reel.

"LET IT GO!"

"Good God almighty," his father said. He threw the fish into the water and stepped toward Aaron, for a moment, his hands out like he wanted to grab him and bash his head on the rocks. "What have you done?"

Aaron waited for it to come, certain his dad could do it, because of what his mother had said about him. He'd just seen his dad kill something, without ever imagining it were possible before.

Slowly his father bent to pick up the pole, in his father's face, something dark that made Aaron step back.

"You had to ruin it?"

"You weren't listening, dad."

His father looked up at him, a shadow on his face, behind him the river glistening so bright it was like a mirror throwing sharp light into Aaron's eyes. His father straightened himself, holding the broken fish pole, the hook dangling. "Listening? Your mother always said listening. You have to ruin a good time, like I have these growing off trees?"

His father came toward him, a big shadow looming up, the pole swinging in his hand, like he would haul off and hit Aaron. Aaron ducked back, and his father came at him, swearing, "You think it's some little thing, huh, break a man's pole!"

"You weren't listening," Aaron cried out, stumbling backward, trying to find the words. "Maybe next time, dad... if you listen... it won't go wrong."

His father stood before him, huge, shaking, somehow holding himself back.

"If you only listen!"

And then his dad swung, not so much at Aaron, but at the air, at himself, stumbling backward, shaking his head, cursing. It was his father who cried out, staggering sideways, jerking his hand. His father bent over, swearing. He held his hand to himself. Stuck in his palm was the fish hook.

"Sonofabitch!"

His father pulled at the hook, "Owwwww!" But it wouldn't come loose, the flesh in his hand rising with the hook. "It's stuck in there, goddamn, it's barbed."

A deep groan twisted his father's face, his hand shaking. Aaron reached for the hand, blood flying, spattering him.

"Get your goddamn knife out."

His dad held out his hand, a scared look in his eyes, like he couldn't do a thing for it.

"Son, you got to cut the hook loose. I'm faint around my own blood."

Aaron trembled, terrified at what his dad wanted, if he could even do it.

"Goddammit, son, you got to do it for me. I'm faint."

His father half-fell back on the rocks. He laid his hand out before him, his face lowered, shaking, as if crying. Aaron quickly managed to open the blade, and where his dad showed him, against the palm, in one clean slice, Aaron cut the flesh down to where he felt the blade scrape hook.

His father groaned, and Aaron felt his father grip him madly, pulling at him, thanking him. Squeezed into a fist, the hand dripped blood. The hook lay free on the rocks.

Neither of them said anything for a moment, Aaron with his dad leaning against him, head and shoulder against his waist, the two of them watching the river, the sunlight on its surface breaking up between the dark pool and its silvery riffles.

Sweet Silent Gray
Robert McNally

He was the first to take me through a cloud, this uncle
married to father's sister who was fated to put her head
in an oven. She was still alive that summer afternoon,
just home from a third trip to the sanitarium's
electroshock chamber, when he banked hard left,
nosed down, said, *I'll show you what it's like,*
diving toward a cumulus as white as ice, as polished bone.
He smiled wide, became again a bomber jockey in Korea,
leveled when nose plowed into cloud. I expected
solid, braced hard as the vapor folded us
into gray, swallowed the engines' pulse,
and subtracted Ohio below. *Now that's a cloud,* he said,
pulled slowly up, banked easy right
back toward the open and the sun.
He knew I was delighting
at the lightness of it, and I wonder often
whether he told her about that cloud, whether
her head entering the oven's mouth
longed for that very softness, wanted the same
sweet silent gray.

Moonlight
Sara Bernard

The icy moonlight glows in marble waves, gleaming pearl white over the contours of her cheekbones and dust gray in the shadows of her eyes. Her nose and fingertips are ruddy; her breath steams; the ghostly billows fade toward the frosty stars. A sparkle of the moon's face shimmers in her eye for a moment.

I'm looking at her through my clouded eyes, through a face contorted in confusion and pain; the tears sweep down my cheeks and leave drying streams of ice. I rub them furiously with cramped hands then stuff them back into the worn pockets of my jeans. We sit in silence: a frigid silence, the iciness of the night carving its way across the chipping windows of our minds. But she seems comfortable, even bored: she sighs briefly, pulls a pack of cigarettes out of her pocket, and slides one between her lips.

"Want one?" she queries in the muffled and familiar tone of one whose mouth is preoccupied, but the sound falls like melting snowflakes onto the still air and fades like the steam into blackness and silence. I don't hear her, but stare blindly, piercing my vision into the abyss of the gloom until I can almost feel the dilation of my pupils. She shrugs; the sudden flame of her lighter cuts at my eyes, snuffing out the moonlight in its orange warmth. Hot smoke curls richly upward and devours in shifting outlines the weak vapor of our breath.

I need a tissue.

I wonder what sluggish movements her mind is making. I wonder if I'll ever see her again... I wonder if she cares... or if there's a way I can stop. My eyes are stinging.

"Look," she begins.

But she doesn't continue. She takes several slow, drawling drags of the cigarette, and wraps her musky flannel tighter around her narrow frame. She won't look at me, nor I at her; I pick at my shoelaces and the straggling strands of my hair, I rub at my eyes and trembling lips; she inhales strongly and exhales coolly, and places her forehead in her hand.

"Look, I know you're totally confused, or whatever."

I rub my eyes harder.

"But I can't just... I'm not... I mean, you can't *hold* me like I'm your doll or something, and dress me up in ribbons and, like, expect me to...expect me... You all expect me to be something I'm not."

I can answer her; I only bury my head in my knees and scrunch up my face until it hurts.

"I don't wanna waste my life... I can't just stay here and let everything, like, consume me..." She pauses again, and takes a long drag, and glowing starlet fingers scramble up the paper shaft. She flicks some ash at the darkness. "Everything is so—*you* know—routine...day in, day out, go to school, then to work, then home...and everywhere I go I'm surrounded by everybody's stupid expectations. Everything is pressure...and competition...and reputation. School is a joke—they make us get out of bed at the most ungodly hours so we can go insane with endless busywork, and come home again so we can go insane with *more* endless busywork...and those brainless amoebas who attend this penitentiary do just as they are told, while making life miserable for whoever doesn't confirm to their idea of beauty, grace, intelligence...what you wear, what you look like, what you do after school, who you hang out with..."

She clenches her fists and grinds her teeth and grinds the end of her cigarette to a furious pulp, and casually pulls out another.

"Don't *do* that!" I cry suddenly with difficulty, my lips stiff with the chill air. "You just *had* one. You shouldn't smoke so much...."

She glares at me through the murky shadows, and viciously slams her thumb onto the stubborn lighter switch. Blowing streams of smoke into my face, she snaps, "You're just like everyone else. That's what they all say. 'You shouldn't smoke so much, you're ruining your life...' What do you really know about my life? What the heck do you really know about *me?* You have no idea how much I smoke. I happen to *not* be a smoker. I happen to *eat* vegetables. You're all such a bunch of stuck-up prudes."

I know she's not speaking to me directly, yet it chills me all the same. The moon has moved a little, and the shadows are different, dimmer somehow. I begin to shiver uncontrollably. My cheeks feel tight and dry, encrusted with tears and grime. *Isn't the moonlight terrible?*

She gives a grunting sigh of exasperation, and her hand is shaking so she can hardly bring the cigarette to her mouth. "I can't live here anymore... I just *can't*. I can't stand *anything*. I can't stand those ridiculous teachers. You'd think I was a machine or something. 'Why didn't you *write* an essay in a night? What's this, you *have* a life?'" she mimics in a piercing nasal whine. "I'm sorry I just *go* to this freaking school, I'm not some pickin' magician. It teaches me nothing. I go there to be harassed every single day, and I can't stand it one minute longer..." Her voice raises a pitch, and becomes breathless, reeling off words in tumbling excruciation. "And even—even if, for a teeny, tiny, microscopic moment," she squeaks, her voice dripping sarcasm and tears, "I've felt all right with things, that just means it'll all come crashing to the ground sooner or later. God, and when he did that to me, I"—with a strangled gulp—"I just can't be that perfect! I can't look like her, have her hair, her eyes, her body, and get straight A's, and a soccer scholarship, and perfect teeth, and"—but before she can finish her voice cracks with a dry sob. For a moment she seems barely six years old—small, frightened, alone, childishly unhappy—her voice and hands shake and wobble, her face crumples. I nearly expect her to stick her thumb in her mouth; but it is a cigarette instead, and she is abruptly herself again, cool, calm, composed, sophisticated. "You don't know me," she says icily with a forced swallow, and turns her nose slightly upward. "No one really knows me..."

I close my eyes. The cold breeze is tugging at my hot lids, congealing tears into stiffened crusts of crystallized sorrow. Eerie shapes dance like swirling specters in the blackness behind them, in rhythm with the thud of my heartbeat and the throb of my temples.

"You can't just leave 'cause of that...'cause you're afraid..." I say, twisting my hands around my knees.

"I'm not..."

"I don't always feel like I fit in either, that doesn't mean you..."

She leaps up, her body bristling like a cat's, her eyes hurtling lighting jabs at my words and my stomach and my soul, till I cringe in anguished pulses and turn away as if to ward off a blow.

But she stops. She is crying, pouring silent tears which slide down her hollowed cheeks to drip forlornly off her trembling chin. Her body shakes. "You know what?" she snaps. "You can just go. Just go."

I shake my head and softly hold out my arms to her—pleading, loving—but with a violent jerk she turns and sprints into the lonely house, slamming the door with a bang that echoes forever.

I stand numb, unable to move nor think nor breathe. Another slam, and then the rapid screech of an old engine catching. I keep my frozen perch for hours, an unthawed icicle, Juneless and pure, under the cold gaze of the terrible moon.

Lullaby and Goodnight
Charlene Villella

As I open a jar of dill pickles pictures float up
with the tart smell of cucumbers and dill
I see wood stoves sweating heat into enclosed back
   porches
Clear glass jars lined up like soldiers that
shine in the light coming through screens
bisecting them into small squares
Lid piles that spill over counter tops
circles the color of gold like pretend bracelets
small hands sneak them off one at a time
Dark orange rubber seals like flat tires
from tricycles that sail through the air
then roll in small orbits on hard wooden floors
scrubbed three shades lighter than the walls
and baskets of small cucumbers like dark
green exclamation points that perfume the air
and bring saliva running into mouths
Grandma stands at the stove as small hairs escape
the confines of braided bun to glisten white in sunlight
She mixes alum.....dill....water into a tart brine
that will pucker mouths and make jaws ache

She sings the songs of the day in raspy contralto
as she packs jars with cucumbers and adds dill
then cloves and anise....pours hot brine over them
caps them with a seal then screws on a ring
and lid....lowers them into boiling water
eight jars at a time in the metal holder
waits until the lids snapped down with a click and a
small inward bowing then goes to scrub the next batch
As I watch her scrub the cucumbers I remember the feel
of stiff bristles on my knees and elbows
She scrubs each of us with the same crisp strokes
then tucks us away....me in bed....cucumbers in jars
I wonder as I wander outside if she sings them a lullaby
    too
before she leaves them in the dark

Beware the Stranger
Fred Norman

It's a Thursday night, the evening before my 35th wedding anniversary, and I'm at Stoneridge Mall in Pleasanton, California, to buy an anniversary card. I enter the mall through the second floor Nordstrom door that opens onto the men's shoes section, and spend several minutes looking at the displays. My shoes, like me, are old and have holes in the soles, but the several different pairs of shoes I see that I like are all priced above $250, and I move on feeling older than when I entered the store. Two hundred and fifty dollars! For a pair of shoes? To think that I paid $125 for my first car. Gas was less than a quarter a gallon. Little girls smiled at strangers. And I fell in love with my wife on our first date.

I leave Nordstrom's and head toward where I think the Hallmark store is. A woman pushing a baby stroller is meandering in front of me, her daughter dancing by her side, and as I start to pass them on the right, the stroller slides into my path, so I slow and move to pass them on the left, but here the daughter angles away from her mother to block my progress once again. But I'm not in a hurry. I smile at the little girl and she smiles back at me. She's about two, I'd guess, at the walking-stumbling, zigzag stage, cute, happy-looking. She looks up at me again and I smile at her again, but this time she doesn't smile back at me. Instead, she frowns and moves quickly toward her mother's outstretched hand, but I walk past them thinking of my children when they were her age, her frown not registering, not intruding on my pleasant thoughts. In front of them, my back toward them, I hear the little girl say, "That man was looking at me, mommy." I remember my daughter saying almost those exact words once at a party, in a room filled with people she didn't know—strangers—one of whom was playing peekaboo with her from a distance. My daughter had a sly smile on her face, a mischievous look in her eyes, expressions that were mirrored by the stranger, a good friend of mine who became a good friend of hers. The memory causes me to grin, and I forget the family behind me and think about a family years ago at home.

Where the corridors intersect, like the little girl, I zig when I should have zagged, turn left, not right, and only after fully circumnavigating the entire second floor of the mall do I discover the Hallmark store. And by chance, I find myself approaching the mother and her daughter once again. They're not too close this time, and I hardly notice them. Only later, outside the mall, do I recall the mother picking up her daughter, holding her protectively, and scowling at me. For now, I'm filled with happy thoughts, and the only things I see are happy scenes.

There are hundreds, if not thousands, of cards in the store, but only one is perfect for my wife, and it takes me many minutes to find it. The envelope is purple-periwinkle, one of her favorite colors. I feel elated. I feel alive! I feel that I'm doing something she will really like, something important, although only important to the two of us, like a secret, and at the checkout counter, the young saleswoman senses my mood and smiles. She looks at the card, and then at me, and for a moment we share a silent pleasure. I pay. We speak ten words or less, but each of us sends to the other an unspoken message about the inherent beauty of marriage.

I walk out through Nordstrom's, past the $250 shoes, almost to the exit doors, and there, for the third time, is the mother and her daughter. A man is fiddling with the stroller, collapsing it, perhaps. Or there may be a smaller child in the stroller, and the man is wrapping it up, so to speak, to protect it from the colder air outside. I'm not paying attention. I have my own thoughts. I vaguely recall having seen the mother and the daughter and the stroller, with or without smaller child, twice before, but the recollection is more subliminal than conscious. They could be—they are, in fact—total strangers, but being civilized strangers, the man and I each hold open a door for the mother and her daughter to pass through. I'm not looking at any one of them in particular, just holding the door until I know they're all outside, just looking up at the stars in the sky. "Thank you," the mother says, but I don't reply because I think it is the man she has thanked, and I let go of the door and walk toward my truck.

Yes, I'm not paying attention. I'm thinking of my wife and my children, my family, remembrances that began less than an hour before when I smiled at the little girl, but now the little girl brings my attention back to her. I hear her voice, suddenly so familiar, the message I heard before and misinterpreted, the meaning of which I now understand. "There's that man again, daddy," she says. It's almost a whisper, but it shouts a fear that shocks me. I know the man's head jerks around in my direction, but I don't look back. I don't want to look, much less smile, at any member of his family. I don't want the little girl to see me, nor I to see the little girl. What should have been a tinkling silver bell is now tarnished and dull; what should have been the beating of my heart, and hers, is the thud of iron striking solid lead.

It is so sad, that sound of heavy pounding I hear and feel inside me, for it is the echo of reality reflecting off the real world. That little girl has been trained as I would train my daughter were she now a little girl, as I would train my son were he now a little boy, as I *do* train my grandson, who *is* a little boy:

Beware the stranger!

Beware the stranger!

Beware the stranger!

And I forgot. I smiled at a stranger, and she smiled back at me. Just once. Just one mistake.

But whose?

I drive away. The mother is standing by her car. Tall. Protective. She's watching me, and I will my body to shrink into unrecognizable invisibility, to hide in the increasing distance now separating us. I feel ashamed that I should want to hide, but I am afraid. I am afraid of what might happen if this family were to see me at the grocery store tomorrow or if I were soon to unknowingly drive slowly past their house. One more chance encounter might well cause them to take protective action, to accuse me publicly of what I privately find revolting. I imagine that even now, as they drive home, they accuse me. They speak in newspaper headlines, they speak of their own fears, they speak of hoping to see me again, of bringing me to justice, of bypassing justice. And I, as paranoid as they, drive home in fear, afraid of the impossibility of explaining simple fate to complex minds, of policemen knocking at my door, of neighbors staring, of my wife being deep in thought at times when normally she would smile at me.

I awake the next morning and watch my wife open her anniversary card, tenderly careful not to harm the envelope, smiling as she reads the words inside, looking up at me in pleasure, in love with me, and I in love with her. The sun is shining. She and I and the room and the entire house, our home, are bathed in warmth and light. This is the world that we want, and this is the world that we have. But although I smile and laugh with her, it is merely an attempt to convince her that I share her happiness. In fact, I am depressed.

The previous evening's experience still troubles me. I read the newspaper every day, and doing so has made me aware of the long, long list of children who have been abducted and abused. Projecting my grandson out into our larger society makes me aware of the even longer list of children who must be protected from such a fate. But the little girl of yesterday makes me acutely aware of the price that all of us must pay for that protection.

I wonder, for instance, if I should continue to play the game of spying on my grandson at the public playground. He doesn't know I'm there, and I stare intently at him and follow his every move for many pleasurable minutes until he sees me and runs to me shouting, "Grandpa! Grandpa!" For I know that long before he discovers me, others will. Long before I notice the others, they will notice me, a stranger staring at a child.

But what should they do? What should they do if they see me, a stranger, carry him, my grandson, into the men's room at the playground? What should they do if I brush the sand off the dress of his friend when she falls off the swing? What should they do if she hugs me? Indeed, what should I do if she hugs me? What should I do if she smiles at me and waves. What should she do if I smile at her?

I think back sadly to the night before, to that innocent little girl. A concerned but sometimes perverse society tries to protect her from its own perversions, and it blocks the warming sunlight that you or I or any unknown but potential friend might wish to radiate. In the chilling darkness, she may never again smile at a stranger. She may never fall fearlessly in love. No one may ever buy her envelopes of purple-periwinkle, nor know her favorite colors, nor fill her years, or her husband's years, with happiness.

The Woman in the Room in the Building Across the Street

Mélanie Beasley

I decided to end things.

I'd tossed and turned myself out of my warped mind and out of my bed and onto the floor, searching blindly for the pieces of everything and nothing, that was me. My sweaty palms were dried by their exploration of the carpet, the fragmented visions of my sleepless night darting before my eyes. I knelt there on the floor like a panting dog for a dizzying moment, blinking away the harsh realities with relentless force, my heart pumping in sync with the crickets of the night. They were crawling underneath my skin.

And then I found myself outside on the balcony, slapped by the dew-speckled breeze of the early morning, and the reality of myself in this place that had been here yesterday and the week before, and that would be here tomorrow, too. It would probably even be here if I weren't, and the thought bothered me.

The buzz of an invisible car zoomed in and out of earshot. I scribbled my gaze every which way to validate the noise, but the effort was futile. The sleek street below was still but for the watercolors from the stoplights bleeding across the intersection. I swept my glance upwards and around, contemplating the end for the umpteenth time when my eyes snagged on a sudden bright light screaming out of the early morning darkness.

Across the way in another apartment building a room found life. A woman in a billowing black nightgown floated towards the window, one hand clasping a cordless to her ear, her free arm waving about as if she were dancing. I could see her so clearly as she swayed her voluptuous body in and out like an entrancing snake, her rich chocolate hair framing a seductive smile, and yet I couldn't believe that she was there, living, with feelings and responsibilities and experiences totally separate from myself and my own life. My eyes were at once irritated by their intrusion into her foreign world. The uncomfortable realization that anyone in my building could look straight into this woman's private world crawled under my skin. And yet, as grating as her error was on my mind, I could not tear my gaze from its intrusion. I was completely entranced.

I'd lived in my fourth floor apartment for six months and not once had I ever had the blinds open at night when the lights were on. It's always been an irritant, one of those grating things, like sleeping with the closet door open, or standing in front of a peephole after knocking on someone's door. Things like that make me antsy, as if I'm suddenly vulnerable, an open target.

My thoughts disintegrated and my focus returned to the woman in the room in the building across the street. She was still doing the Cha Cha with her phone, her satiny lingerie reflecting the light over glossy hourglass curves. I wondered if anyone upstairs or down below was awake and watching her. I wondered if she cared. Maybe she didn't feel she had anything to hide.

My mind rewound itself at an instant as it returned to my contemplation of the end. Bryan had moved in a month earlier but tonight he was sleeping on the couch. And tomorrow he would be out, and it would be over. After two years of fantastic intensity it would be over.

Or would it? All of a sudden I felt overwhelmed by the eeriness of the dead silent scene alive before my eyes. I knew that when I turned my back on her she would cease to exist. But if I turned my back on him would I cease to exist? Was I like that dancing woman, alive only in the sight of someone else?

I backed up through the open glass door and slid it shut in front of me. It shuddered. My eyes remained fixed on the dancing woman. For a moment then, she stopped dancing to listen to the voice of her invisible partner, but gradually her body resumed its oscillation as she moved to the far side of the room. And then her world was stamped black.

I blinked with the loss of life and then felt thankful that she had ended things before forcing me to eventually turn my back on her existence. And then I turned towards my bedroom door. And my heart melted with the thought of him curled up on that concrete slab on the other side of the wall. He had lied to me. It hadn't been some little white lie. This had been big. Something to end things over. And yet, he had apologized so profusely and so sincerely, had made such an effort to right his wrong. How could I not forgive and forget? Wasn't that what a relationship was all about?

When I opened the door I could see his hunched silhouette sitting on the couch. Though his face was in shadow I could tell that he was looking at me. I wanted to invite him back to bed at that very moment but I knew I couldn't be that forgiving. So I made my way to the couch without a sound.

"I couldn't sleep," he said softly, his gaze never having left me from the time I entered the room to when I sat close beside him on the couch. "I can't stop thinking about what I did, and about how I hurt you."

I sighed heavily. "You lied to me..."

"I know. I don't know what I was thinking. But I promise," he added, softly touching my chin between his fingers, "it will never happen again."

I believed him. I had no reason not to. After two years we had come to know so much about each other –

the quirks, the vices, the thoughts behind the expressions. I even knew when he was lying to me. And right now he wasn't. He was truly sorry, and what had come between us would never come between us again. There would be nothing more to hide.

I stared into those electric blue eyes and the force of the spark weakened me. "Come back with me to bed," I whispered, leaning my nose against his shoulder. I breathed in his scent as though it were my life source.

"Are you sure?" he asked.

I nodded as I reached for his pillow. "Yeah. Come on." He smiled and then kissed me on the forehead, and I felt myself lighten with relief. He was back, and I was myself again. Everything was going to be all right.

The cordless fell to the floor with a deafening thud as he dragged his blanket from the couch. I stared at it for a moment, and for the first time since I'd gotten out of bed I could hear the crickets through the open window. They were crawling underneath my skin. My gaze swept up towards the window and around to him. He was waiting for me. Watching me with those eyes that validated my everything and anything.

I picked up the cordless, set it on the coffee table, and walked over to the window. My hand searched the wall for the cord, grasped it, and pulled the blinds shut for the second time that night. And then I moved towards him, locked my arm in his, and together we went towards the bedroom.

To make a new beginning.

Class With Mr. Betts
Robert Eastwood

He came, a crumpled suit, to school each day,
a full brown briefcase, scurrying as if
on tender feet. I got to school before
the others, solitary, watching, hunched
as Mr. Betts arrived. He nodded once
to my raised hand. My thoughts were never him
but how my life would bloom once I was grown.

In Physics Mr. Betts, his voice in tune—
a thin, squawk-drone he used to fill the hour—
embarked on his instruction with resolve
but seldom looked at us, the rowdy boys
with snickering grins, and wise remarks, too cool
to care or think of Mr. Betts. He taught
as murmurs rumpled the room, the going bet

to guess the times that Betts would thump his nose.
So old he seemed at fifty. Scrawny, thin-
ing tawny hair, a beak-like nose he punched
around. He scribbled numbers on the board
with popping chalk, his anger squelched in dust.
In secret I would hurt for old man Betts.
I dreamed of ways to take his part, to stand,

to bear his burdens well, and speak for him.
So long ago. He must be long deceased.
I think of him when looking now about
my classroom filled with murmurs, grins, and when
I search for one at least whose eyes are warm,
though he may settle in his seat and score
the times my knuckle knocks against my nose.

The Martini Glass
Dana Cohn

A tear formed in his eye as he lifted the broken martini glass from it's resting place on the mover's packing paper. Damn them. Why couldn't those movers be more careful? His precious things meant nothing to them. All the insurance money in the world could never replace this broken glass. Only a few pieces had broken off of one of the glasses, but he knew he would never be able to look at them again. He slowly shook his head, and with one piece of the broken glass in each hand, thought back to that day nearly ten years ago when they had bought the mismatched pair of martini glasses.

The day was warm with a slight breeze. Venice had the best weather in all of Italy, and this day was no exception. Sunshine bathed them as they disembarked from the train at the *Stazione di Santa Lucia*. They had been touring Italy for a month, seeing whatever they pleased, never rushing from one city to the next. Lingering a few days longer in Rome to see the ruins that he loved so much. Cutting short the visit in Milan which had seemed to them like any other big city. Too much like home. So when they got off the train in Venice with no place in mind to stay, they weren't concerned. They sipped a cappuccino at the station, checking the tourist guide for a *pensione*.

"This one looks good," she said. "Private bath, quiet side street, and not too far from here either."

When they found the *Pensione Seguso* on a back alley far from the bustling *Piazza San Marco*, they knew they had found a treasure. The proprietor greeted them warmly. He offered cookies and coffee while he explained about the different rooms and rates.

Wonderful, they told him. This would be the perfect hideaway for their stay in Venice. Wandering around this back alley, they would be able to see a side of Venice generally missed by the casual traveler. They had noticed a little cafe a block or so away with outdoor tables overlooking a small canal. Children were noisily playing ball against a thousand year old church wall nearby. There was no telling what else they could discover about Venice from this location.

They carried their bags up the three flights of narrow steps and admired the tiny room with a view of the neighbor's roses. The furnishings were antique. The linens crisp and fresh. They stepped into the tiny bathroom and laughed about the shower head directly over the toilet. They agreed that this place had been a wise choice. And as he had wanted to rest and read a little before dinner, she would go for a walk and explore the neighborhood.

She walked down the three flights of stairs and stepped once again into the bright daylight. It was then that she noticed the glass blowers directly across the street. Somehow she'd missed the shop earlier in their search for the *pensione*. She eagerly stepped inside to watch the glazier. His handiwork amazed her. Never had she seen such an exquisite variety of glass-blown objects. There were many to choose from, but the mismatched pair of martini glasses with an elephant on the stem of one and a swan on the other caught her eye.

She was still lingering outside the store when he emerged from the room a half hour later. He kidded her about her walk. Couldn't she get farther than across the narrow street? She wanted to show him the remarkable works of art inside, but he had no time for looking now. He was anxious to get to the *Tratorria* for dinner.

"We'll come back to look later," he told her. "There'll be plenty of time."

Reluctantly she followed, wondering if the glasses would be there when she returned. But they didn't made it back to the glass blowers shop that night. After lingering over a gelato and one last cappuccino amid the late night diners at the *Piazza San Marco*, they took the *vaporetto* back to their little side alley and wearily climbed the stairs to their small room long after midnight.

The sun shining through the small windows awoke her early the next morning. Sneaking out quietly, she walked down the narrow alley to the cafe for some hard rolls and orange juice to bring back to the room. On the way back she stopped again to gaze in the glass blowers window. The two hand blown martini glasses were still there, and this time she stopped to buy them. This would be her remembrance of Venice, of this magical trip and the unique, out of the way neighborhood they had found. She so carefully packed and repacked them on every stop they had made throughout the remainder of their Italian holiday, never closing her bag until the pair were safe and snug inside.

And now they were hopelessly broken. As he gazed at the broken glass, he felt as if he had broken her all over again. But she wasn't broken, he knew, just gone. A chapter in his life ended. Down to selling the house and moving out. But not moving on. How could he bear to move on without her? When she became ill, he never lost hope. He would not let himself think of a time without her.

Her most precious possession, the beautiful hand blown martini glass, was shattered, the same as his life had been when she died. A tiny drop of blood swelled in his hand as he grasped the broken glass, not realizing how hard he was squeezing. He looked at the blood and dropped the glass. As it shattered on the ground, he lifted his bloody hands to his face and sobbed.

Long Haul

Charlene Villella

For years we knew him as
the man who drove trucks
the man we met
in the middle of the night
on lonely stretches of road
where we brought him clean clothes
and picked up his dirty ones

Sleepy-eyed children in Disney pajamas
standing barefoot on cold tar roads
waiting for a kiss and squeeze
from the tall thin man
that drove in and out of our young lives
in metal monsters that growled menacingly
and belched smoke that smelled of rotten eggs
from two tall metal stacks on the cab
Headlights glared down long empty roads
as cattle stomped and moaned in the trailer

We watched mom hold him and kiss him
until we got bored and curled into
small balls on the rear seat of our old Buick
and dreamed of fathers who lived in houses
Came home each night
ate dinner at tables
instead of booths in truck stops
and smelled of aftershave
not cattle and diesel
Read bedtimes stories
and said I love you
instead of
see you next week

A More Gentle Type of Minotaur
Kevin Deenihan

I've often felt that the whims that come into my head are synchronized somehow with the clouds above me. Tendrils of thought somehow conspire with tendrils of dissolved water to send me off on tangents while I'm walking down some random city street. Nothing extreme, nothing like me deciding to strip naked on Market Street and attempting to fly. Whims like that belong to those who enjoy certain substances more than the fancies of flying clouds. My whims are more along the lines of when I decided, on Tuesday, to go look for love. This happened two months ago on a cold morning.

Other whims of mine were to ride the cable cars and act like a stupid tourist, wondering which bridge is the Golden Gate and which is the Richmond Bridge. Going to Alcatraz and sleeping there overnight, careful not to get caught. Sunbathing on the top of one of the larger buildings. Eating nothing but chocolate. Stupid stuff, I know. But when someone lives a humdrum, standardized life for 15 years, it breaks up the monotony.

I am a male. Since I have no proof to offer of my age or my degree of beauty, I won't try to force it on anybody. My name, I'm sure, will come out in my narrative in a short time, so there's little point in revealing it here. Think of it as a mystery—life is more fun with mysteries along the way. This is all anybody needs to know about me.

Ironically, my idea to go look for love came soon after I was sunk in thought on ugliness. San Francisco is not a pretty place if a visitor ignores the people. Without the life and impulsive smiles of an indomitable people, the unfortunate effects of constant fog on ramshackle architecture become apparent. A hit or miss attitude towards garbage collection also contributes to a city that sometimes is less than beautiful—that can be frankly ugly. Ordinarily my path to my livelihood, a banker in the Steel Pyramid, takes me past the genteel glass of the Library, into the Financial District. Today, due to some errant cumulous cloud messing with my head, I found myself instead trekking down an urban backwater near Chinatown, musing on the rundown appearance of life.

Generally a good liberal, I had out of self-preservation erected defenses towards guilt. It occurred to me that if I walked out of this block of melting concrete with any sort of angst, I'd end up volunteering time already committed towards some worthy cause. I already do worthy causes, and one more wasn't going to resurrect the more shining ghosts of San Francisco past, so I cast about with my fly-fisher mind for a more constructive idea. Love hit with a force that caused me to suspect a large cirrus cloud was behind it. Bankers have a tendency to lose out to Bikers in single bars, and my work had kept me from considerations beyond high finance. I wondered whether this latest urge was biological or social in nature. It didn't seem biological, as there was no particular urge to found a race of little bankers in my soul. A guy who has, without fear, taken the only senior girl left with braces to the Senior Prom has no social aspirations. Perhaps it was merely curiosity.

First I finished my business in the steel anthill known as the TransAmerica Pyramid. A bull market had caused whimsical minds like mine to become a golden commodity. I would buy large amounts of unlikely stocks, and they would quadruple in value. Yesterday I had taken a hunch on a stock I thought was rife for speculation, and the hounds of Wall Street has bid it up to twice its value. The boss was pleased, arranged for a bonus, gave me the day off. Omens are well known to all financial specialists, so I took the hint and decided to follow through on my desire for love. Oddly for me the whim hadn't gone away. I still wanted to feel the communion of souls so celebrated in the world.

Method was my first concern. I tended to go at things in a logical way, the intent being to reach my aim the fastest. As utilizing that method would lead me to the red light district, a different method was called for. Primitive methods of mating rituals really didn't appeal to me either. I wanted a soul mate, I wanted one quickly. Disguising what was a liberal, hardworking banker in clothes or cologne wouldn't help me. Alcohol wouldn't assist either. I decided on a compromise methodology. Instead of going up to people endowed with two X-chromosomes and saying, straight out, "Lets be soul mates and love each other," I would be more circumspect in my affections. It wasn't that I didn't think the first method wouldn't work. This was, after all, Baghdad by the Bay. Women who would respond with an "OK, let me get my stuff" were not the type I was looking for, unfortunately.

A coffeehouse was my chosen hunting ground. Finding one was easy. To find a coffeehouse in San Francisco, all one has to do is sit down, anywhere. A coffeehouse with comfortable chairs will spring up immediately before a visitor's butt gets close to the ground. Just for perverse jollies, I ordered tea. This time the man on duty had been around for a long time and knew what tea was. Teenage worker bees sometimes think I just have a weird fixation with the 20th letter of the alphabet. I found a good vantage spot and sipped Earl Grey as my plan worked through my head. My hunting grounds had already been poached on. Tired but still apparently virile failures from the

80's were talking intently to bored women. The balance of power had shifted quite a bit during my 15-year absence from the dating scene. The unmistakable hunter aspect was apparent in several femme fatales, with the slightly smiling prey the one with chest hair.

Something about my long-time celibacy must've communicated through, as none bothered to approach my lonely table and cooling tea. I was just as well. My sensors for love were flashing "she's not here" into my head. My whim had taken on a stronger life than I had usually seen, as this seeming failure greatly disappointed me. Instead of giving up, however, this deep compulsion fought back my obvious thought to return to an empty apartment and the ministrations of Chef Boyardee. I was to continue looking. She was out there.

So I went coffeehouse-hopping, feeling like quite the 90's man. Feeling strange that I had set my heart on something besides financial markets. I was a whimsical person, I prided myself on it, yet here I was with this strange peculiar need in my heart. Not a want. A want was giving in to buying Ben and Jerry's at the supermarket. This was a need. A need that sent me forth like a modern day Theseus, seeking a more gentle type of minotaur. Jason seeking a golden heart instead of a golden fleece. The chaos of it all confused me. My whims allow me to escape a humdrum existence, but they are not bulwarks against the 8 to 6 workday I normally lead, when not making a killing on Net stocks.

I was in line in Starbucks for about my 6th tea of the afternoon, when my scanners registered a target approaching. She didn't walk in haloed by a ray of sunshine. She walked in under a cloud, and I didn't miss the significance. The ring finger of her hand was unencumbered by that damning mold of cast-off metal known as a wedding band. Relaxed, not waiting for anyone, she seemed unconcerned with anything other than a drink and a break from the rodent race down a two way street just outside. I took my seat for the 6th time, gazed at her, not without a good dollop of the masculine disposition towards mental undressing. My attraction wasn't an object of lust. It was something else. Maybe the Shakespearean sudden fall of souls. Maybe, I was willing to allow, wishful thinking. Something.

Fifteen years of celibacy had left me with only the slightest idea on how to pick up a girl. Fifteen years of celibacy had left me with an MB in Finance and a tendency towards escapism, which was better than most, but I needed to breach the walls of social convention that, I was sure, were the only things standing between me and my soul mate. The compulsion stripped my rustiness away from me with the skill of WD-40. With a casual swagger that would've impressed the most skilled of pimps, I strolled up to her and introduced myself. She didn't fall into my arms and quote love poetry, which I was sort of hoping for, but she didn't grunt noncommittally either, which I considered a good sign. We spoke a bit, my hopes that my love was standing in front of me growing.

They plunged quite a bit when her boyfriend walked in. He was a nice guy, we spoke a bit, then I politely excused myself to go throw up once or twice. On the porcelain throne I cursed myself and tried to disperse this still hungry compulsion that called for love. Need was scaring me. I had my good job, my nice apartment, my little fantasies. Why did I need some mystical connection with another person? Once composed, I slipped out the front while my quickly ex soul mate watched her boyfriend adoringly.

I have a date this Friday, my first in 15 years. We met in the same coffeehouse, at the same table. I came up to her, more guarded this time, and no boyfriend intruded. Me, the left-brained banker, is trying his hand at poetry and flowers. The clouds weren't putting whims in my brain. That's ludicrous. All they are is collections of evaporated Pacific waiting to ruin a new wax job on my car. All they were trying to do was help me find things more important than banking, until I found the one thing that was.

Her name is Christine, who I hope will become Mrs. Scott Holiday. That's my name, that's my personality, and that's what happened when I looked for love on a Tuesday. Wednesday would've worked, too.

A Fine Spring Day
Jerry Gervase

A friendly spring sun warmed the stone tables outside my favorite restaurant basting the park-like setting in its yellow juices. While I sipped a mocha and plumbed the deep ideas of a famous Poet Laureate a man carrying a pet transport cage sat down at the table next to me.

A lady wearing jogging shorts walked towards me down the narrow path between the outdoor tables. She broke my concentration as the sun glared from her white thighs. I looked back to my book but her jasmine scent lifted my nose from the book again. Someone said: "Hello beeper!"

A white cockatoo, with a blue plume winked at me from the pet carrier. A lady in black sweats carrying two salads joined the man at the table. "Hello beeper," she said. "Hello beeper," the bird said again. The life the Laureate infused the pages with could no longer compete with the life going on around me.

The bird's blue and white feathers reminded me of the blue and silver ribbon worn by the little girl on the front page of the Chronicle. She is one of five grieving teenage girls in the picture. She is wearing a light blue pullover and jeans and wringing a shapeless Kleenex in her hands.

Her long brown hair, hanging down her right shoulder, falls to the edge of her shirt. The rest of her hair flows back over her left shoulder opening her entire face to the camera exposing her grief to a world whose attention is focused on her high school, named for the dove-like flower, *Columbine*.

She is fragile, dove-like; and if I knew her name I would say that's what grief's name is. I would put away sad tolling bells and crepe, and sickly sweet lilies and send back to their convent veiled nuns intoning "*Dies Irae*," because her day of wrath is sculpted to her face in an endless lament for her youth and her youthful friends.

I run my fingers over the newsprint but her expression doesn't change. I wish I could reach across the mountains and wire services and hold her and tell her everything will be all right even though both of us know it won't be all right for a very long time.

The poet says in his book that pleasure leaves the mind quickly so it is hard to remember. He does not say that grief lingers. He doesn't have to. The girl's face says it better than any poet can. I want to say something silly to her, something to make her smile, something like "hello beeper."

But she may never smile again.

I've Always Been Good At Solitaire
Ashley Tacheira

We sat as unfashionable children on the carpet
In our groups that had already formed
And as we saw our lifelong bonds created,
I waited politely for everyone else to choose
What those bonds would be
Stranded on the outside

But I've always been good at solitaire.

We grew a little, and our cozy yet separating carpet
Transformed into desks
And I got an award I deserved
But told my mother I was sick that day
As to avoid the attention

This familiar place, with adoring teachers
And cold-hearted children
Soon faded away
And the real challenges began
I'd never seen them, they'd never seen me
But I told my mother I was sick everyday
Because I really was

I've always been good at solitaire.

I was finally accepted
And finally saw my "lifelong" bonds created
But it's funny how people change
And "lifelong" sometimes means "not long enough"

But I've always been good at solitaire.

And this place of sporadic acceptance faded away
And I was left stranded on the outside
Surrounded by those with "carpet bonds"

But I've always been good at solitaire.

We read the play, *The Diary of Anne Frank*
I was never Anne; once I was Margot
Peter called himself a "lone wolf"
The girls with perfect makeup giggled
Their boyfriends obeyed and followed

But I didn't
I understood

I've always been good at solitaire.

Gold Mountain
Bob Bruno

Li Hue Jung stood in the restroom, his left hand on the open stall door, right foot raised in midstep. The object hunkered in that stall stunned him. As his teeth worried his lips and his mind tried to get around what he was looking at, Li Hue Jung couldn't help thinking how far away from home he had come.

This was his second trip outside his village, Weihui, in the foothills of the Kunlun mountains, and his first trip outside China herself. Already he had witnessed wonders that none in his village could even imagine, starting with the airplane itself. How could such a giant, ill-shaped thing fly? It was big enough to hold what looked like hundreds of people. Probably more people than in his entire village. And how did those wing things ever stay on? The airplane had air, and food, and there was even a movie! Who'd have ever thought?

When he had exited the plane there were even more wonders to behold. There were restaurants. He had seen restaurants on his trip to Luho city but they were hovels compared to these. And there were sculptures, and works of art. There were even indoor sidewalks moving up and down, here and there. The truly amazing thing was that he'd only been here, in San Francisco International Airport, for an hour. If all these marvels were contained just in this airport, what then must the rest of Gold Mountain hold? Gold Mountain truly was Gold.

Li Hue Jung enjoyed himself tremendously while waiting for his nephew to pick him up. Riding back and forth, up and down on the moving sidewalks, a grin eating up his face, and noting everything for stories to give to his family and friends, Li Hue Jung realized a pressing need develop. Seeking a restroom, he puzzled over that word. Although his dictionary assured him that restroom was indeed a toilet, he couldn't understand why anyone would want to rest in the same room in which they relieved themselves. Well, he found Americans to be rather inscrutable anyway.

Entering the restroom he was immediately impressed by the vast expanse of tile, the gurgle and burp of running water, and the marching line of urinals. These last he was familiar with from his visit to Luho. He had seen men urinating in them, but had never seen so many in one place. Those he could deal with. It was when he opened the door to a stall that Li Hue Jung almost fell over.

Puzzlement furrowing his brow, he moved to the next stall and swung open the door. And the next. And the next. And in each stall stood a massive, winking, odd-shaped hunk of porcelain. Li Hue Jung had not seen such a sight even in the great city of Luho. They had normal toilets, porcelain lined, yes, but still basically a hole in the ground. It seemed a shame to despoil such a lovely work by defecating in it but his need was great. Mounting the toilet, feet firmly on what seemed to be a lid, but had a hole in the middle, Li Hue Jung squatted with arms resting on the top, and wondered why Americans seemed to make everything so complicated.

5:53 p.m., Easter Sunday
Susan Browne

I sit in my lawn chair,
which is plaid and coming apart,
strips of the weave unweaving,
while I bask in the last of the sunlight,
which I found by the door to the laundry room
and beside the anonymous bush
with the flowers petaled
like spokes of a wheel
and the crayon yellow
I knew as a child.
And now I remember
my Easter dress
and the yardage department
in J.C. Penney's basement
where my dead mother and I are walking,
moving slowly down the aisle of cotton.
The sky is the color of her eyes,
and at my feet, the pile of pine needles
I swept up and forgot
because I wanted the last of the sunlight
and the various songs of the birds,
especially the long clicking
that repeats every two seconds
and must be a mating call,
because I'm feeling sexy
staring at the water meter,
its glinting pipes and bolts and knobs,
and at the shivering (a little wind now)
apple and silky plum.

The patch of sunlight is shrinking,
but the iris has plummeted up
among weeds and wild raspberries,
purple flames licking out of green stalks,
and it's cold, the sun gone behind the pines,
their green darkened by dusk,
and it's time to go inside on this Sunday
when everything is resurrecting
from winter, from memory, from loss.

Armistice Day Duck Hunt, 1940

Teresa Brandt

In Winona, Minnesota, Armistice Day, 1940, is remembered as the day a fierce storm changed the lives of hundreds of families who lived near the Mississippi River. Its early gusts encouraged hunters to flock out to the marshes, lakes, potholes, and ponds of the mighty river. Its piercing cold and fatal gales left a permanent impression upon their community.

The ducks hadn't flown down from Canada as they usually did each fall, flocking to the soggy islands and inlets of the Mississippi on their way south to avoid the harsh cold of the north. After weekends rowing their skiffs in vain through the currents of the river, hunters came home empty handed. Instead of golden-breasted ducks for Sunday dinners, wives substituted farm hens or smoked sausages from the icebox.

There was talk, though, that on Armistice Day, the ducks were coming. Leon Bronk, Jr. heard it from his friends at the Brom Foundry, and after church on Sunday, it was the main topic of conversation. On the night before November 11, he cleaned his shotgun, packed a good lunch, and the next morning paddled over to an island near Twin Creeks before the sun slit the horizon.

Hundreds of other men did the same. They planted canvas-protected bodies in sand pits and damp gullies. Gusts of wind, promises of the ducks' imminent arrival, blew in from the South and West.

About eleven that morning the ducks came, their bodies propelled by the wind as they soared over the hunters' heads. Thousands covered the sky like a swarm of disturbed bees. The men pointed their shotguns at the flocks, took aim and fired repeatedly. Could hardly contain their joy as bushels of feathered bodies fell to the ground. Leon was so preoccupied he didn't notice at first how fierce and cold the winds had become.

His hands became so stiff he couldn't hold his rifle anymore, much less point the barrel and shoot. He started to pick up the dozens of ducks around him, but lost interest as the winds threw him to the ground and curled down his neck into his bones.

Within just a few hours, temperatures dropped more than 50 degrees and winds reached 80 miles per hour. Water skated over the river like sheets of glass and soaked Leon and other hunters on the unprotected island. Angry waves beat their canvas-cloaked bodies and gripped them with a hurtful cold. Their fingers numbed, their faces became frost-bit.

Leon and five men used their boats as shields against the wind. With their rifles, they shot boughs from the trees. Lit a fire. Around them, winds blew snow into steep drifts as the daylight waned and night froze the island.

Some of the men couldn't take the cold. Between the makeshift hut of the skiffs, they hurt so bad they left its shield against the wind and crawled into the river to find warmth. Beat their hands until they were bruised and blue. Lost feeling in their limbs—and lost their lives.

The rest of the men huddled around the fire. They pulled the boats closer together for more protection and waited in bleak darkness until morning brought relief to the icy temperatures. When winds relaxed enough, they started for home.

As soon as the sun came up along the Mississippi River, relatives gathered at boat docks for news of their men.   Planes droned overhead searching for life and dropping packages of sandwiches, whiskey, and matches where they found it.   Parties of men in boats with broken motors paddled with difficulty out to the islands.   They returned with chilled and shriveled hunters, breathing but frozen with dreams of death.

Leon rowed up to the Minnesota City boat dock by himself.   His eleven-year-old son, Paul, watched him guide the canoe alongside the pier, stiffly throw its rope around the post, and crawl onto a safe ledge.   He looked beaten, hungry, blue and hurt, but alive.

As his dad walked awkwardly across the planks toward him, Paul's thoughts turned to the night before. After listening to storm news all day, his mother had knelt her five children down in the living room and started praying the rosary.   One by one, his brothers and sister had fallen asleep on the floor.   When Paul climbed the stairs to go to bed, she was still awake and praying, slumped back into her chair, but filling the room with verses of hope.

Returned to Gabin
Noam Lupu

On November 1, 1995, my grandparents, uncles, mother and I returned to the town of my grandmother's birth, Gabin, the town she left in 1939 when she fled Nazi persecution. For 56 years, Gabin was no more than a memory for my grandmother, until the day she returned to Gabin.

At about 12:30 p.m., we reached Plock, driving through it in our southern route toward Gabin (pronounced Gombin). My grandmother could sense that we were approaching her town, forests of birch trees leading the way. They were the beautiful trees she had told us so much about, the trees she remembered fondly as the entrance to her home town; the trees beneath which her family spent so many weekends; the trees that hid her and her sister as they fled to Russia.

My grandmother was on the edge of her seat when we saw the white road sign containing the five letters that meant happiness, memory, regret and horror to her: G-A-B-I-N. We drove to the town square and looked for the magistrate of Gabin. We were to deliver a letter to him, hoping he would be kind enough to show us around town. After ten minutes of little success finding the street, we parked next to the police station and questioned an older man passing by. He took us around the corner to the magistrate, Zbigniew Lukaszewski. Mr. Lukaszewski was just then arriving from work, his wife awaiting him at the door to begin dinner. My grandmother began to talk to Mr. Lukaszewski in the Polish tongue she struggled to remember.

Mr. Lukaszewski went inside for five minutes, then joined us to navigate in our van. He took us first to the Jewish cemetery, our primary point of interest, passing by the area on which stood the synagogue. My uncles seemed to pay little attention to the aging building which stood on the land where the Gabiner Jews prayed. Both my grandmother and I turned around and looked at the site as it got smaller in the distance.

For a moment I could see the marvelous synagogue of Gabin. I saw the rabbi walking into shul in his long black coat and black hat. I saw the men wearing woolen hats and vests, followed by the women, their long skirts and colorful blouses radiant in the summer sun. I saw the stairs that lead the women up to the balconies.

I saw my great-grandfather solemnly walk into the great wooden building. He was holding the hand of my grandmother's brother, leading him into the Yom Kippur service. Just before entering the synagogue, my great-grandfather stopped and slowly turned around. He looked at my grandmother and their eyes met. That moment is suspended in time in my memory. At that moment I saw the past and present collide, in a town where so much of the past had been eliminated.

I saw the ark inside the synagogue, a beautifully crafted work of art. I saw the rabbi open it as Kol Nidrei was chanted. The silence in the sanctuary was deafening. The rabbi's voice was quivering, trying to finish the moving tune. My great-grandfather listened carefully, mouthing the words. He was confessing his sins, asking God for forgiveness.

I saw the bimah, its golden poles and wooden steps. From it, the rabbi recited the repetition of the Amidah while the men swayed, hunching over their books.

"Prosto...prosto," directed Mr. Lukaszewski in Polish as we neared the outskirts of Gabin. My uncle obeyed, stopping in a muddy road next to what seemed to me like the middle of nowhere. There were three oak trees standing tall atop a tiny hill, a footpath leading through them. We put on kipot and got out of the van. In our hearts we were quietly consoling my grandmother. Mr. Lukaszewski led the way up the hill, from where we could see the Jewish cemetery. It was a scene like none I had ever seen.

Never in my wildest dreams had I imagined such disgrace could fall upon such sacred ground. Only a handful of broken tombstones lay alongside the overgrown grass, between trees. There was no marker, no attempt to convey the holiness of this land. My grandmother did not cry, but a look of sympathy came to her eyes. Maybe she felt pity for those buried beneath the ground. Or maybe, deep within her heart, she was fighting the pain of memory.

A man on a bicycle rode by the cemetery, not even looking in its direction. He paid no attention, not even respect, to the cemetery just inches away from the wheels of his bicycle. Five chickens crossed the muddy road and strolled around the cemetery land. I felt empty, lonely, abused. Here, Judaism had been forgotten.

Suddenly, my great-grandfather appeared in the cemetery. I could not tell whether he was close by or far away, but I could see his face. He looked young. His features were prominent, his hair neatly combed. His expression was serious, stern and upset. His eyes were overflowing with tears, but he held them back and simply stared at me. He did not look at my grandmother, and I do not know if she saw him.

Slowly, he walked toward one of the tombstones and knelt down, gently setting down a flower before rising. I looked at the flower, a beautiful red rose. Its petals were vibrant with color, its leaves strong and healthy. Yet one by one, the petals began to wilt and fly into the air, carried away by the wind. Slowly the green pigment of the stem turned to brown, then yellow. The flower turned to dust, blown away into the atmosphere.

My heart raced. I looked to my great-grandfather, but he was gone.

Fighting against time, we decided to continue our trip. Mr. Lukaszewski took us to a little room in the Gabin library. There, he took out a few files from one of the drawers and showed my grandmother to a small table. He showed her page after page of material documenting the Jewish culture that thrived in Gabin.

There were photographs, official documents, lists, maps, everything the Jews had left behind. It was all there, but *they* were not. We all looked at the documents quickly, promising Mr. Lukaszewski that we would find a way to obtain photocopies of them. They were an amazing tribute to and documentary about the Jewish culture and lifestyle that once thrived in that small shtetl.

We took Mr. Lukaszewski to dinner at the only restaurant in Gabin. My grandmother sat quietly throughout the meal. She looked pensive. I knew she was thinking about her family, her friends, rekindling old memories. Her head was probably racing with thoughts and emotions. I sensed my great-grandfather entering her thoughts, the father she left behind so many years ago. That look of sympathy returned to her eyes.

We left Mr. Lukaszewski at his home and followed his directions to the Jewish school. The short yellow building, now serving as one of two public schools in Gabin, was the Jewish school my grandmother attended. I could imagine her sitting in one of those little rooms beside her friends and neighbors, studying Polish and Yiddish. My grandmother strolled around the area. She stopped and stared down a street, which looked like a tunnel, covered by trees that arched over the pavement. It was the street that led my grandmother to and from school every day of her childhood. She had told me so many stories about that street—walking to school in snow, rain and far below freezing temperatures. When we then decided to drive to my grandmother's street, she was able to give us directions. After all these years, my grandmother was still able to show us how she got home from school.

So in two minutes, we reached the square on which stood my grandmother's house. The street was still called Ogrodova. There, my grandmother's parents owned a store, where they sold baked goods and general supplies. I could imagine all the people working on that square, constantly moving. The bakers, the tailors, the carpenters, the butchers, the businessmen.

The actual buildings were no longer standing, but there was something in the air, some memories left in the atmosphere of this desolate place. The park in the middle of the square looked cold and abandoned. All around, not a single person could be found, not a single voice heard. All were gone—the bakers, the tailors, the carpenters, the butchers, the businessmen.

I took my grandmother out of the van and together we walked around the square. My grandmother suddenly stopped by a pair of old stone columns. They looked out of place, unnecessary. My grandmother stared and gradually began to weep, a look of remorse in her eyes. "These were the gates to my friend Aliza's house." I looked at the stones. A glow came to my grandmother's face. She moved towards the stones. I put my hand on her shoulder. She embraced me with one hand; with the other she felt the stones. Her fingers moved up and down, as if caressing the concrete.

Aliza Holtzer's house was gone. A cottage now stood in its place. The whole street was full of new houses. The homes of the Jewish working men who struggled to sustain their families were all gone. Nothing was left.

My grandmother turned around and looked at the park in the middle of the square. Remorse and sympathy returned to her eyes. She began to weep. I embraced her. She shook her head, never taking her eyes off the park. "It used to look so alive. There were children playing in the park, people walking around. Now it is all dead. There is no life her anymore." There was nothing I could say.

We climbed back into the van and drove away. It was already completely dark outside. The ride back to Warsaw was quiet. Most of us fell asleep, but my grandmother stayed awake. Memories she had long since repressed were returning to haunt her. And with them, they brought pain. I sensed her pain. I wanted to help her, but I could not. I wanted her to tell me exactly what she felt, but she could not. I knew I could never completely understand or share her pain, and I thanked God. My grandmother could not sleep that night...and neither could I.

Today, when I close my eyes, I see the streets of Gabin. I see my great-grandfather standing beside a cobblestone road. The street is empty, my great-grandfather stands alone. I am standing next to him, but he does not look at me. He looks old now, leaning on his wooden cane. I call to him, but he does not hear me. I lift his wrinkled hand from the cane and support him with my arms. He looks up at me. A tear trickles down the side of his cheek. I do not know if it is a tear of joy or sadness, but I know it is divine. Slowly, he fades away into nothingness. Then the streets fade away, and I suddenly find myself back where I was.

Joe Bellino's Thighs
Contest Judges

Joyce Gunn (Adult Fiction) received her Masters in Library Science from Rutgers University. She is Acting Deputy County Librarian and wrote a section on storytelling for the deaf in a revised edition of *Storytelling: Art and Technique.*

Bill Harlan (Adult Fiction) is the former Director of the Center for Higher Education in San Ramon, CA. He is the author of *Probes: An Introduction to Poetry.*

David Wright (Adult Non-Fiction) teaches creative writing at Las Positas College. He created and oversees the Las Positas College Spring Literary Arts Contest.

Keith Warden (Adult Non-Fiction) is former editor of the Pleasanton Business Connection and writes for several San Francisco Bay Area Newspapers.

Fred Ostrander (Adult Poetry) has been published in many magazines. His book *The Hunchback and the Swan* is published by Woolmer-Brotherson. He currently is poetry editor of *Blue Unicorn.*

Linda Watanabe-McFerrin (Adult Poetry) is a poet, travel writer, and fashion merchandiser. Her work has appeared in numerous newspapers and magazines. She is the author of two poetry collections, *Chisel, Rice Paper, Stone* and *The Possibility of Redemption is Something We Hadn't Figured Out.*

Contest Judges Continued

Toni Rimer (Teen Fiction and Poetry) writes the *Around Pleasanton* column for the Valley Times, and she is a personnel specialist for the Dublin Unified School District.

Kathy Moore (Teen Fiction and Poetry) is a teacher and writer. She is a member of the Society of Children's Book Writers and Illustrators, and she runs the popular Mother-Daughter Book Group at Rakestraw Books in Danville, CA.

Judging Coordinator: Jerry Gervase

All pieces were submitted to the judges anonymously.

The Across the River Writers Roundtable

It has been almost a decade since the *Across The River Writers Roundtable* was founded to serve the needs of aspiring writers and appreciative readers. Since the beginning, the monthly meetings have included food, readings, critique, and solid motivation to complete and perfect writing projects. As the 90's fade and the millennium emerges, the group continues to lovingly explore writing and to strongly encourage reading.

The ARWR has refocused on the process of writing, readings, and quarterly "Evenings of Literary Enjoyment" featuring local authors and a special theme. Group membership includes two (2) copies of the current *Griggs Anthology*. All net proceeds support the programs of the Writers Roundtable and the ARWR Scholarship Fund.

Tantalus – A king in classical mythology who, as punishment for having offended the gods, was tortured with everlasting thirst and hunger in Hades. He stood up to his chin in water, but each time he bent to quench his thirst, the water receded. There were boughs heavy with fruit over his head, but each time he tried to pluck them, the wind blew them out of reach. (Dictionary of Cultural Literacy)

Origin of the term "tantalizing."

Text Paper: Georgia Pacific 55 lb. Westminster Trade Book Cream.